# THE BOY JOHN LETTERS

# THE BOY JOHN LETTERS

## Sidney Grapes

Introduced by Keith Skipper

The Boy John Letters by Sidney Grapes

© Mousehold Press, 2003

First published in volume form by Norfolk News Co., 1958
First collected edition published by Wensum Books, 1974

This edition first published in 2003 by
Mousehold Press
Victoria Cottage
Constitution Opening
Norwich, NR3 4BD


Reprinted 2004
Reprinted 2008


Cover design by Terence Loan


'A Country Funeral' from *The Best of Jonathan Mardle*,
reproduced by permission of Prospect Press


ISBN 978-1-874739-29-6


Printed by Wrightsons, Earls Barton

# CONTENTS

Sidney Grapes was a rustic comedian, garage prop
an outstanding Norfolk character with the evergree

While problems in setting down Norfolk speech preoccupied many other
leading figures, Sidney happily combined written and spoken entertainments
in an appealing and enduring style, lending it colourful and constant support.
His legacy is rich and inspirational. It cannot be too fanciful to suggest his
Boy John Letters have done as much as anything to keep alive Norfolk's vital
sense of individuality in an increasingly grey world. Certainly, they have lit
the way for a whole generation of local entertainers seeking to stay true to the
traditional Norfolk credo – dare your listeners to get there first and then milk
the moment as you finish together in a lather of laughter.

Sidney had made his mark as the archetypal Norfolk comedian at local
concerts and dinners long before he dropped a few lines to the *Eastern Daily
Press* in January 1946, the start of a twelve-year exercise destined to reach
a far wider audience. The Boy John Letters, all the more eagerly anticipated
because they were infrequent, were written in dialect but never swamped by
it, and composed by a countryman who wrote as he spoke and spelt as he
pleased.

The cast list soon became household names: Boy John, Granfar, Aunt
Agatha and the cantankerous Oul Mrs.W—. Many readers, myself included
when I discovered them in the early 1950s, used to cheat a little and turn
to the 'PS' first for Aunt Agatha's latest example of homespun philosophy.
Favourites are still regularly exchanged wherever Norfolk people meet and
want to break the ice, from cocktail parties to darts club outings: 'PS Aunt
Agatha, she say: "Reality is when you leave datty dishes in the sink an' they
are still there when you git hoom."'

Early epistles were full of post-war austerity as rationing and shortages
drew weary sighs, but a twinkling humour drawn from the very heart of
country life shone through from the start, and those of us weaned on such
homely humour can scarcely believe they are half-a-century old, especially
when audiences still fall under their spell at a harvest supper, village concert,
or family reunion. The appeal goes much deeper than a predictably refreshing
dip into nostalgic waters.

Collections of these letters have sold in their thousands. The first batch,
produced in a little yellow booklet by the *Eastern Daily Press* shortly after
Sidney's death in 1958, saw an original run of 5,000 shoot up to 12,500. It was
sold out by Christmas. *The Boy John Again*, a second collection in a little blue
booklet, met continued demand shortly after, while the first complete edition
of the letters in 1974 was also greeted with considerable eagerness.

This fresh delivery for the twenty-first century underlines their abiding
attraction. They may be rooted in time and place, but they retain genuine

charm and value because they are wholly unpretentious, gently amusing, and admirably self-effacing.

Sidney Grapes lived all his life in the Broadland village of Potter Heigham. He started work at fifteen for his father, a carpenter and builder. A bicycle shop developed into a garage and motor business with the increase in traffic to the Broads, and the coast. Sidney was the first to accept that holiday traffic weakened the dialect even if it did boost the economy! He lived with his wife Ella in a little flat above the garage. They called it Uptop.

Eric Fowler, who wrote with great distinction for the *Eastern Daily Press* as Jonathan Mardle, recalled that off-stage Sidney had little more than an ordinary tincture of Norfolk in his speech, 'but the important point about him was that Norfolk was his native tongue. He was village born and bred. He knew intimately the sort of people he was writing about, and met them every day.'

On stage he wore an old 'chummy' hat – a soft felt hat with a narrow brim – a smock and a 'ropper' round his neck. But those tempted to dismiss him as just another country bumpkin with a few tales to tell soon discovered he was not such a fool as he might have looked.

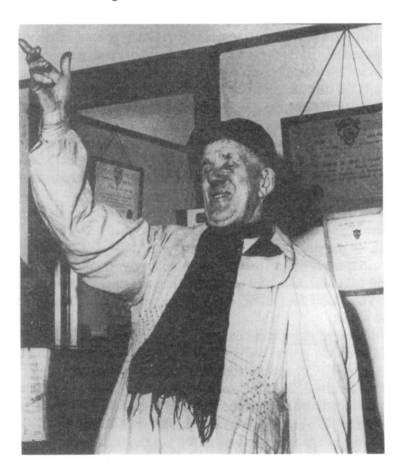

'He would get the audience laughing at him half-way through a story, and then up would come the admonishing forefinger – "Now, hold yew hard tergether!" – and he would proceed to the cream of the joke in which the rustic triumphed and had the audience laughing with him.'

While praise close to home has followed the Boy John Letters down the years, helping turn curiosity into adulation at many a local function, it was a remarkable cultural coup when they were lauded a few years ago at a conference in Helsinki! Peter Trudgill, Professor of English Linguistics at the University of Fribourg in Switzerland, and an international expert in the field of dialect described the letters as 'work of not a little genius'.

> Not only are the characterisations and vignettes of village life brilliant, and therefore enormously popular, but Sidney Grapes is also a superb writer of the local dialect, right down to subtleties such as Granfar speaking in a more conservative, traditional way than the other characters.

Yes, Professor Trudgill is a proud Norfolk lad – and president of Friends Of Norfolk Dialect, the flourishing body set up in 1999 to promote and preserve the vernacular – but his scrutiny of the close link between language and society is seen as a key weapon in the fight against a culturally standardised world.

While humour is a key component in Norfolk's continuing battle to 'dew diffrunt', the Professor warns that if dialects are to survive they must be used in as wide a range of contexts as possible.

> The Norfolk dialect is a vital means of helping preserve Norfolk values, culture, way of life. It is also important, more than many other dialects, since it is one of the last dialects in the south of England, and especially the south-east of England, to remain relatively distinctive and relatively widely spoken.

That sort of academic interest and support lends considerable weight to the campaign against directing Norfolk dialect towards the obituary columns. I doubt if Sidney Grapes expected to be in the front line of such a campaign when he composed that first letter and sent it to the local paper in 1946. But it blazed such a telling trail that his influence was bound to be felt long after the final epistle was printed in April 1958.

To the first-class stamp of 'endearing' can be added the shiny label of 'enduring' as Boy John and his country cohorts continue to deliver the genuine Norfolk goods.

**Golden Memories**

It is hardly surprising that such a colourful character should prompt so many good yarns from those who saw him on his entertainment rounds or simply caught up with the latest gossip when they dropped in at his garage.

Sidney's Broadland business expanded with another garage near Potter Heigham bridge where several men were employed running hire cars and taxis for weddings. Sidney served his last gallon of petrol in June, 1957, before retiring.

Bernard Durrant of Poringland recalled visits to the garage in the mid 1950s when he was assistant to the county council's weights and measures inspector Eric Westwood. The department aimed to test all petrol pumps once a year – 'but we seemed to call much more frequently than required. Mr Westwood and Sidney appeared to be good friends.'

They exchanged jokes and tales, but Bernard's main reason for strolling down memory lane was to reveal one of Sidney's unusual interests: 'He collected sugar beet. In those days the beet was dumped at Potter Heigham bridge to be loaded on to barges which were then towed to the factory at Cantley. Many of the lorries carrying beet called at the garage for petrol. Every year Sidney took a beet from the first lorry to pay a visit. He labelled it with the date and name of grower. He then put it on display. When I used to call there were a large number going back many years displayed in the garage. Most of them were so shrivelled they were smaller than carrots!'

Retired journalist Dennis Barker outlined how his father, Lowestoft businessman George Barker, gave Sidney his first chance to enjoy the Boy John Letters in performance, as distinct from the printed page. 'Having a passion for all new technology as well as old Norfolk dialect – he was born in London but spent almost all his life in East Anglia – my father must have had one of the first wire recording machines. He decided to record with his own voice in Norfolk dialect all the Boy John Letters then available. He took these to Sidney at Potter Heigham, who was as delighted as a child to hear his characters come to life, nudging my father in the ribs as he remarked on what the characters were getting up to, almost as if he had never met them before, let alone created them!'

Sidney's roles as churchwarden and member of the choir at St Nicholas' Church in his home village has drawn a big crop of wide-grinning reflections.

Sheila Smith of Hemsby joined the church choir in the 1950s. She recalled how Sidney 'used to tell us funny stories during the sermons and we tried not to laugh out loud'.

Mervyn Hinton lived at Potter Heigham when he was a lad. 'Whenever Sidney travelled to the west of the region he would take my father with him as we emigrated from Lincolnshire in 1936. His car in those days was a Standard 8 or 10. One Sunday evening a crowd of us local boys stuffed grass up the exhaust as it stood outside the church. Funnily enough, I can't recall the outcome!'

On the touch-line for a football match at Potter Heigham in the late 1940s, Sidney felt moved to have a word with the home goalkeeper who had been beaten eleven times.

'If it's any consolation, young man, you had royalty watching you this afternoon."

'Oh, and how do you work that out?' asked the bemused youngster. 'Well,' replied Sidney, working overtime to keep a straight face, 'if you're a goal-keeper, I'm the King of Siam!'

Patricia Munday of Caister remembered Sidney as a friend and customer of her parents, Vernon and Violet Le Neve-Painter, who kept the Falgate Inn at Potter Heigham from 1934 until 1954. 'I once had the privilege of appearing on the same programme as him in a concert at Wroxham Village Hall in a "Wings for Victory Week" during the war. My choice of song was a little incongruous but popular at the time – "In My Arms". Sidney's wife Ella had tried to persuade me to sing something more suitable, but I insisted on my choice. I was so nervous it took three introductions before I could start to sing.

'Seven years later Sidney was responsible for me taking part in the Wilfred Pickles programme "Have A Go!" on BBC radio when it visited Potter Heigham in September, 1950. I well remember Violet Carson at the piano - she later became Coronation Street's snug-dragon Ena Sharples - and Barney Colehan who "gave me the money". I also went on to win the jackpot and took home the princely sum of three pounds, seventeen shillings and sixpence, a fortune for me in those days.'

*Sidney Grapes in his washerwoman outfit*

A knitted version of Aunt Agatha, the homely character at the heart of the Boy John Letters, was created by a church group at Potter Heigham and then acquired by the late Edna Nobbs, who accompanied Sidney at the piano for many of his concerts. Aunt Agatha found her way to Spalding and the home of Marjorie Ostler. Sidney was her uncle by marriage: 'Aunt Ella was my father's sister.' Marjorie returned the knitted Aunt Agatha from her Lincolnshire holiday with this message pinned to her apron: 'Please accept her with my good wishes. I'm sure she'll feel much more at home in her native Norfolk.'

She took up residence in a corner dedicated to Boy John in the Museum of the Broads when it opened in her home parish of Potter Heigham. Now the museum is housed at The Staithe on Mill Road in Stalham - and Aunt Agatha is there with her homely ways.

**One Good Turn**

A couple of books in an envelope marked 'Uncle Sidney's Entertainment Literature' prove how much time and care went into a Norfolk act which had audiences rocking with laughter for so many years.

The books were sent to me by Marjorie Ostler from Spalding, the smaller one inscribed: 'Sidney Grapes, The Limes, Potter Heigham'. This would have been used before 1915, the year he married Ella, as Sidney's parents lived at The Limes. It features songs, recitations, and words and lines from favourite yarns. The second volume, much larger with 'Petty Cash' on the cover, is packed with information about the well-oiled routine still doing the rounds as the Boy John Letters collected their own massive following.

Sidney filed his favourite yarns under various headings – country, local, washerwoman, general – with a few words to serve as reminders of their full contents. Some of the jokes still jump off the pages and ask to be given a fresh airing. For example, the question 'How would you like to be up in that plane?' demands the answer, 'Well, I shouldn't want to be up there without it!', and the reference to 'muck-carting' points firmly to a touching agricultural scene as two old labourers look forward to sharing duties when it comes to this important job on the farm. One turns to the other and says: 'Well, I'm a'gorn ter drive – what are yew gorn ter dew?'

Other abbreviations leave much more scope for guesswork, even among those who profess to have a fund of well-loved Norfolk stories. Picking a page at random, I tried these for size: 'Vicar and invitation – market, where's mother? – old woman's tooth out – can't hear your sermons – shooting gallery – I shan't be with you coming back – persuaded man to bet on other horse – glass eye more sympathetic – hit me harder – his holiday did him good – three men in a pub, 72, 82 and 92 – egg-timer – where do you keep your money? – first bus ride to Norwich.' You can make up your own rustic routine out of that lot!

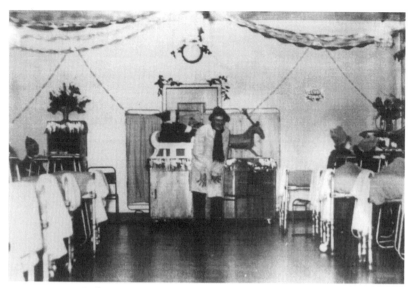

*Sidney Grapes entertaining in a hospital ward*

At the front of Sidney's main reference book, a new sheet provides a fascinating potted autobiography as well as a few more pointers to the way he sorted out his act. 'I write my own songs,' says Sidney, 'and never use any make-up. I have never asked or advertised for an engagement – all have come from recommendation. I find audiences very interesting; I just feel my way and give them tales I can see they appreciate.'

He reveals how he often put on two shows a night at local concerts 'Transport – a cycle, frequently doing a double act with my friend Herbert Woods and, later on, another double act with Bert Wall, using a motorcycle and sidecar as transport.' Reflecting on his schooldays, he admits: 'I got into minor troubles for fooling, but got off lightly as my master, the late F. Goldsmith, had a keen sense of humour.'

Scores of admirers sent me versions of Sidney's musical party pieces, so I melted them down into the following lines. He may well have changed them himself from one village stage to another. In the first song he would dress up as an old washerwoman ready to wring as much squit as possible out of a busy week:

> Monda', I'm a'workin' at the washtub,
> Tuwsda', I'm allus ironin',
> Wennsda', I'm a'charrin' at the village pub,
> Tharsda', I'm a'cookin' all the family thar grub,
> Frida', I'm a'packin' for the market,
> Yew'll find me at the stall Saterda',
> An' the only time I git a bit o' rest
> Is in the arternewn on Sunda'!

When he sang the following at a village hall concert, a large lady in the front row was most upset because she thought Sidney was singing about her. 'He wuz lookin' streart at me!' she complained:

> Mary-Ann sheer dun wi' me,
> Anuther young man she's got, yer see,
> But he'll sewn tire o' har upon his knee.
> Bor, she weigh forty stoon, bor, she dew,
> Can't ride a bike, she is tew fat,
> When she git on, the tyres go flat,
> There's no bigger fewl in the wald 'n me
> An' he's got my Mary-Ann!

A more romantic theme in this verse, and children were always encouraged to join in the last line with gusto:

> Mary-Ann, she look luv'ly,
> My hart, she look well,
> An' me? Well, jest look at me
> Dunt I look a swell!
> We meark a nice cupple
> Dew Mary an' me,
> I'm twetty-four an' she's
> Jist twetty-three.
> As we walk down the aisle,
> All the people dew say:
> 'Why, John married Mary-Ann,
> Hip-hip-hip hooray!'

Of all yarns told by Sidney, this one emerged a clear winner among his ardent followers. Again, different people have different ideas as to how the vernacular should be committed to print, so I give the story my own treatment. Several enthusiasts say they heard Sidney tell it on the wireless just after the Second World War:

> Me an' ole mearte Jimma cum up ter Norridge larst week an' went inter one o' them pubs in Ber Street. While we wuz in the pub I git inter an argerment longer sum o' the customers an' they hulled me out.
> Jimma, he cum out ter see how I wuz. I say ter him: 'Bor, I'm a'gorn' back in there an' I'm a' gorn ter hull them blooks out one at a time. I want yow ter stay out here an' count 'em as they cum out.'

Nut long arter I go back in, blarst, a body cum a'flyin' out. Jimma haller, 'Good on yer! Thass one on 'em!'

I tanned over an' look up at Jimma. I say, 'Wuh, yew silla fewl, thass me agin.'

## Among the Pews

Sidney Grapes lived through sweeping changes in his home village of Potter Heigham as it flourished and grew into one of the three capitals of the Broads holiday trade and boating industry. Along with Wroxham on the Bure and Oulton Broad on the Waveney, Potter burgeoned as Herbert Woods, who built his first motor cruiser in 1925, developed the biggest hire fleet on the Broads.

Of course, Sidney added to the village's fame after the Second World War with his Boy John Letters and glowing reputation as a rustic entertainer. Older inhabitants still call it 'the Boy John's village' and a new development called Grapes Close serves to keep his name to the fore. It is in the beautiful parish church, however, where his memory burns the brightest.

The oldest part of St Nicholas' Church, with its round flint tower and thatched roof of Broadland reed, dates back to the twelfth century. Sidney was a chorister here from his boyhood and a faithful churchwarden until the end of his days. By his wish, the church was decorated at his funeral, as if for a spring festival, and joyous hymns were sung.

*St Nicholas Church, Potter Heigham*

Later in the year an oak-panelled clergy vestry was built in the parish church and dedicated in Sidney's memory by the Rt Revd Percy Herbert, Bishop of Norwich from 1942 until 1959.

Here's the address from that service held on Sunday 23 November 1958:

It is no sermon which you need today in this simple service, but rather that I should, if I can, sum up the thoughts that are as much in your hearts as mine, to pay a simple tribute to a very wonderful person, as we gather here today as friends of Sidney Grapes.

Many of you were his neighbours, who saw him day by day, others of you have come from a distance because you wanted too to share in a tribute to his memory, and you will feel that nothing could have been more fitting than that we should shape that tribute in the dedication of this panelled vestry, beautifully designed, quite admirably made, worthy of the church, and standing fittingly, for all time, as a memorial to him.

Sidney Grapes was in the minds of most, if not all of us, the very perfect symbol of a Norfolk Countryman. He looked it, and he was rooted so to speak in the soil. He lived here all his life, he was part of this community. The village found itself so to speak mirrored in him, and he regarded all those simple things of village life entirely satisfying. He didn't hanker for the bright lights of the city streets, or those modern inventions and excitements that have produced such a restless and rootless society. He loved the old way. He saw the life of the village and farms around: and how much he thought about the old people all the time – and the neighbourly friendship of it all; the kind of thing that has made England what it is, has given it its stability, given it its character. There will never be anybody who loved Potter Heigham more than Sidney Grapes did. He loved its surroundings, its characters, its traditions, and his love for it made many of you who knew him well appreciate it more than you ever would have done without him. For you too it became a live place to live in and be thankful. I mean not just Potter Heigham, not just its roads and its houses, but rather that old traditional life that it represented. And to show that love, that deep appreciation, he created something entirely new, and something of quite outstanding value.

His Boy John Letters, now happily collected, at least many of them, and published together were something quite unique. There never had been anything quite like them before. I don't think there will ever be anything like them again. Nobody has ever done anything quite like this. Not only lit up by delicious humour but made us as we read the letters laugh aloud, wherever we might be, but giving an entirely living picture of simple village life. It is not given to many writers to create fictitious characters that are so alive, and that once met with, will never be forgotten. Granfar, Aunt Agatha, Old Mrs.W—, we know them, they are our friends, he made them living people, each with their own special character, but each the kind of people that we felt we'd known all our lives.

He takes his place in that sense with the immortal characters invented by Charles Dickens and I don't at the moment recollect any other writer who did that with quite such success, and lasting success. To read those letters is really to be enriched, and then to go on our way with the new courage that they breathe all the time, and a new joy in our hearts that we should be alive. Somewhere or other in them he said 'If I can give some pleasure to some people I'll be doing some good in the world', and that's not a bad motto for that whole series of letters, and I think it's that in them that we so much appreciate.

He really did give us pleasure; indeed he did do good in the world. Many of you, of course, knew him much more intimately than it was ever possible for me to do. But I did know him. I did love his simple honesty and goodness, and I counted him a very real personal friend. Maybe the secret of that simple, kindly, happy character lay in this church where he was a constant worshipper, always taking his place in the choir Sunday by Sunday, a friend of all who came, and giving his quiet witness to a Christian faith that lay really at the root of his whole outward character.

He was not only an astonishingly fine natural humorist, he was an incomparable teller of good stories; these things are what the world outside no doubt thought, but we who knew him better, thought of him not merely as people say, a character, but as a good man, whose goodness helped other men to believe in the possibility of goodness. Need one say more? Has not one said all that any of us would hope might one day be said of us?

So we thank God for him, and we pray that in remembering him, we may face the life that lies before us with something of his quiet courage, something of his belief in the goodness of things, with something of the kindness to other people that he showed all the time.

And what he would like us to have most of all, a smile in our hearts.

The last Boy John letter to the *Eastern Daily Press* was published shortly before Sidney's death, but his final helping of Norfolk dialect humour – a menu with tasty hints on good table manners, sufficient to put a smile in the heart of his readers – was published posthumously. Copies of that menu were sold to pay for the oak vestry that bears his name.

Keith Skipper
2003

# MENU

Means – Me an yow can start eaten now

---

## GRAPEFRUIT

Dornt teark it up an bite it, use yer spune.

Spit thar pips unind tha tearble.

---

## OXTAIL OR ASPARAGUS SOUP

Dornt call it bullocks tail or sparrer grass,

and dornt sloup it.

---

## FRIED FILLET OF PLAICE
## TARTARE SAUCE

There's a hull lot on yer ount want much sorse,

Youre got enuff a that all riddy

---

## ROAST CHICKEN

Hev a pearper bag ter slip the boones in, then yow can

knaw em clean when yer git home, or wrap em up in

yor hankerchief (that is if yow hearnt got a cold)

## GRILLED BACON – STUFFING

Dornt expect eggs wi yor bearcon

Yow ount want much stuffin, youre a duen that now

## CROQUETTE POTATOES

These are crooked tearters, mashed up

## GARDEN PEAS

Use yar spune fer these if theres no one a looken

dornt use yor knife

---

## GLACE FRUIT MERINGUE

Dornt lick it – use yer spune

---

## BISCUITS AND CHEESE

Bring yer own onyun

---

## COFFEE

Tearst juss like corfy

---

Yow may smoke now (if someone give yow a fag)

# THE BOY JOHN LETTERS

Best Wishes
from Sidney
Xmas 1932

# A RUM CHRISTMAS

January 2nd, 1946.

Dear Sar— Yow did print a message in yar pearper, a wishin all yar readers a happy Christmas. Well, me and Aunt Agatha, an granfar, thort as how we wud be sum o' the fust to rite an wish yow, an yar staff an orl, a werry happy New Year.

Aunt Agatha, she a took yar pearper ever since that fust come inter our willage. Granfar he like them gays, wot yow have on yar front page. You had a good 'un a few months back, that wus the picture of some cows a feedin on a green with a pub at yin ind o the green. Aunt Agatha she liked the cows, an I liked the willage green, an you can guess wot cort granfar's eye.

Some o them letters wot they rite to yar pearper are orl rite, but a hull lot on em they are allus a mobbin a sum one.

Aunt Agatha, she thort they were awful election time, she said, 'If half wot some on em say about the others is true, well, bor, there earnt none on em fit tu be on our parish council (and they're a job) let alone be members of Parliament.'

We had a quiet Christmas. Aunt Agatha, she went up to Norwich for shoppin a few days afore, an she stood in a que for an hour and a half to git a harf bottle of rum, wot she wanted for her Christmas pudden. Well, bor, she cort the marster cold trew a waitin in that que. When she got home, she put her feet straight inter a barth of mustid an hot warter, and had a good tot of hot rum. Granfar, he had a bit of a tissic, too, when he see that rum, an I'm blowed if her an granfar dint finish up that rum so we had no rum in our pudden.

Well, we all fear to think there carnt be a lot to look forward to. Aunt Agatha say when the war wus on there wus peace to look forward, now there earnt. But as she say, we shull har to keep a doin.—Yors obediently,

THE BOY JOHN

# AUNT AGATHA'S DICKEY RIDE

December 24th, 1946.

Dear Sar— Well, the time a'cum round agin for me and Aunt Agatha, and Granfar, to rite an wish yow, and yar starf an orl, a werry Happy Christmas. Aunt Agatha, she say, specially to that there gentleman wot go about a taken them photos o' pretty plearces in Norfolk, he must a' got a bike, to git about like he dew.

Oh! I must tell yow about Aunt Agatha, last Summer. We had a garden fate

15

at the Wickerage, an weeks aforehand you could buy shillin tickets, then save em all up, then spend em on anything at the fate. Well Aunt Agatha, she was wery busy an dint git there till ever so late, an then ewerything wus sold. She had six shillin tickets wot she'd saved, an orl she could spend em on wus on six shilling rides round the field on the Wicar's owld dicker, wot he'd lent for that purpus. Well bor she cum home orl o' a muckwash – she looked a job.

Granfar, he mobbed har, and he called har a silly old fule. He fear to ha been a pearkin tru a hole in the fence an see har. He say, 'There she wus a bobin up and down on that old dicker's back, a' holden har hat on wi one hand, an har teeth in wi the tother, she look disgustin.'

Poor Granfar, he mob about everything nowadays. He go down to the pub every nite, he cum back a mobbin about the beer, he say he's right glad when he a' had enuf on it. Aunt Agatha say, 'Well yow put em in.' He say, 'I never put *them* in, I votted learbor.' Well fare you well together, a Happy Xmas to all you wot read this. — Yours obediently,

THE BOY JOHN.

P.S.— Aunt Agatha she say, If you dorn't git orl you want, think of the things yow dorn't want – an *dorn't* git.

## A SAUCER OF COCKLES

January 4th, 1947.

Deer Sar— I fare I must rite an thank Bob, wot cum from Fearkenharn, for arsken me to cum over an have a pint wi him.

Thank yer, Bob, but thas no use o' me a imitaten to ride orl that way – me an my owl bike wud be knocked up afore we got harf way.

I tell you wot Bob, I'll meet yow at Tombland Fair, a tha Saturday. Twelve o'clock at the cockle stall, we'll ha a sorcer or two o' cockles, have a jam round the fare, then have a couple o' harf a tews tergather.

You know Bob, me an yew an Nelson and Bill Edrich, orl belong to Norfolk, an we're proud on it, arnt we?

Oh, Granfar, he a got suffin wot plearse him a rummin. Thas tha cricket news. He gi-rup o' the mornin', twitch on the wireless, and make us orl a cup o' tea.

Well, bor, as mornin' he was suffin excited about Bill Edrich, a batten an' a bowlin', he go to pore hisself out a cup o' tea. He got the teapot a' one hand an thort he got the cup in t'other – he hearnt. For he made a mess orl over Aunt Agatha's antimerkasar – she was suffin savage.

16

Well I must learve orf, else you'll be a tellin' me 'this here correspondence is now closed.' Well, fare you well tergether orl on yer. I shornt rite no more – not yit.— Yours obediently,

THE BOY JOHN.

P.S.— Aunt Agatha, she say, 'That no use a grumblin', that ownt help. We're got to keep a dewin'.'

## INTRODUCING MRS.W—

January 13th, 1949.

Dear Sar— I haint rit yow lately 'cos I thort yar pearpar wornt big enuf to waste on my bit o' fulery. Howsomever, I must tell yow one o' tew things wot happened afore Christmas.

Well, we all had colds, an granfar sed he wus a gorn to set up arter weed gone to bed and dew his feet in mustid an warter.

Well he did that tree nites runnin; an Aunt Agatha she got suspicious. So the thurd nite she slipped on a few things an cum downstares an copped him proper. He was then a-putten back inter har cupboard her bottle o' rum wot she got for Christmas. She had hid it up, tew, rite behind a couple o' big jars o' her pickled onions; but he found it.

My hart she mobbed him. And next a' mornin granfar had to go down to the pub with sum eggs and sum money an' git sum more rum – (the lanlord at our pub dornt keep hins).

An then Mrs.W—, she come in. Aunt Agatha say thas acos she thort weed got suffin in the house; but she never got northin. She's an ugly woman. Dew you know what? We had a willage social a few weeks back an she wun the furst prize for the woman wot could pull the ugliest face – and she wornt even in the competition.

Well, thas orl for now; fare-yar-well tergather. A Happy New Year to yow, an yar starf, an tew orl wot read this.— Yars obediently.

THE BOY JOHN.

P.S.– Aunt Agatha, she say 'Miracles dew still happen,' for she was a-picken a' oranges on Porlin beach a Christmas mornin'!*

---

*A ship with a cargo of fruit had been wrecked at Sea Palling.

## GRANFAR COPS THE 'FLU

March 26th, 1949.

Deer Sar— I'd 'a rit yow afore about orl them there latters wot a bin in yar pearper about Norfik words, only me an' Granfar an' Aunt Agatha orl copped the flu. Aunt Agatha, she did read the furst lot on 'em to Granfar, only he was a feelin' wery moderate, so he wus short o' the crust. He heard har reed 'em, an' orl he said wus: 'A lot o' bloomin' squit.'

He was wuss than any on us. Aunt Agatha she dosed him up wi' a grate basin o' biled onions an' a strong dose o' medicine for his stumick.

Well, we had to git the doctor in arter that. That Mrs. W— (dorn't yow put her proper name in, Mr. Editor, du she'll pull both o' us for libel), she cum a pokin' a' nose in wen she heard Granfar was sadly. 'Tiss true she brort him a couple o' kippers an' half a jar o' home made jam.

Well, she went up an' had a look at him, an' she say to Aunt Agatha, rite in front o' Granfar: 'Bor, I don't like the look o' him; he look just like my furst husband did, an' in tree days he was gorne.' Well, bor, that set Granfar back a rum 'un.

Howsomever, he's better agin now, an' he ha' took a interest in all them there latters.

Aunt Agatha, she ha' cut 'em orl out to save 'em; the only trouble is, she say that spoil the pearper for puttin' on her pantry shelf for when she spring clean.

Well, fare yow well, together. I shull ha' to knock orf an' gorne feed Granfar's pig – Granfar, he ha' got a pig.— Yours obediently,

THE BOY JOHN.

P.S.— Aunt Agatha, she say that earn't how *much* medicine we take in life; thas wot good that du us wot count.

## THE OLD FOLK'S CLUB

April 7th, 1949.

Deer Sar— We ha' had a rare du in our village. They ha' started an Old Folk's Club, same as was a gorne on well up at Nor Walsham.

Granfar he got an inwitation, he was suffin plearsed. He washed his feet a' tha nite afore, an' cleaned his best highlows (Aunt Agatha did roun the heels), he put on his Sunday suit, washed well roun his neck an put on a new wrapper. He tricalated his self up proper.

He wus orl fit to go when someone come an told us his old pig had gor out. Granfar he couldn't sturer about arter him cos he wus orl dressed up, but arter a time me an Aunt Agatha stowed thar old pig up, she kep a shiggin her apron an hooshed him in.

Well, orf they went. Aunt Agatha she allus go an lend a hand, specially if thas anything to du wi' old people or children. They had plenty o' wittles, a cup o' tea, an orl sorts o' games wot suit old people. Granfar, he wanted 'em to finish up wi' 'Kiss in the Ring' like they use tew (silly old fule).

Our Wicar's wife wus there a helpin; she earnt one o' them there Wicars' wives wot just put the flowers on the tearble, she's a warker.

Our Wicar he had a rare tork wi Granfar, cos yow see he a gor a pig tew; as Granfar say, 'That show you how respectfull a keepin a pig is nowadays.' Granfar he felt self conshuss about not a gorne to church. He say, 'I'd like to cum to church, Wicar, only I'm hard of hearin, I cant hear yar sermons.' (He can hear orl rite wen yow dornt want him). Our Wicar, who like a joke, he say, 'Well yow dornt miss much.' Granfar say, 'No, so they tell me.' As Aunt Agatha say, 'Granfar *allus* put his fut in it.'

Well, thas orl for now. Far yow well togather.—Yars obediently,

THE BOY JOHN.

## A DAY AT THE FAIR

April 2nd, 1949.

Deer Sar— Aunt Agatha, she ha' bin a'doin' well outer har hins' eggs ter year, so she trearted me an' Granfar to an outin' to Tombland Fair last Saturday.

We orl warshed our feets a' the Friday nite an' orf we went a' the furst bus the nexter mornin'.

We had a rare oul jam round the fair, an' my hart wornt that hot. Granfar he kep' a gittin suffin dry.

We see that tity tiney little woman. Granfar he'd a bin a garpin at har now if Aunt Agatha hearnt jogged his memory. Granfar warnted Aunt Agatha to have a go on the 'mat'. She sed she wud a dun twenty years ago (cos she wornt so wide then).

Aunt Agatha took us orl out to dinner. Granfar sed that was orlrite, only there wornt enough on it, so he went out an' had several pleartes o' clockles. An' then Aunt Agatha bought us tew grate big ice creams apiece.

Then Granfar had a go on the keark walk. Aunt Agatha say, 'If that dornt jibuk his cockles up that'll be a rummin to me.' – But he wornt sick.

Granfar met some o' his oul pals, wot he hearnt met for years, an they had a harf pint or tew togather. An' when he cum to catch the harf arter seven bus, Aunt Agatha, she say, 'Yow a got a rare red fearce Granfar.' He say, 'Yis thas dun a jammin about that fair. ' She smiled but never sed northin.

Granfar told Aunt Agatha he'd ride on top a'gorne back in the bus, so he could have a good look roun' the country. I went up a top along a him, an' dew yow know wot, he fell asleep afore we left Norwich, an' he slep' the hull way home.

Aunt Agatha, she brought Mrs.W— a fairen home cos she'd bin a lookin' arter the hins while we were out, a feedin' on 'em, an a gitten in the eggs. Arter she had gorne, Granfar say, 'That fare a rummin, them oul hins a bin a layin' eighteen eggs a day for as larst tree weeks, now the day she look arter they only lay fourteen.' But my Aunt Agatha she dornt suspect nobody o' nuthin.

Well fare yow well agin togather. –Yours obediently,

THE BOY JOHN.

P.S.– Aunt Agatha, she say, 'That wery oul sayin' – "We shornt git no fine weather till arter Yarmouth Fair" – is orl wrong ter year.'

## KILLING THE PIG

April 30th, 1949.

Deer Sar— Granfar's pig is deard, we ha' killed him inter house, an wornt thar a jorb. There fare to be hundreds a' forms to fill up. Granfar, he mobbed a rumun about them, but Aunt Agatha she filled 'em orl up. She say to me: 'John, bor, there wunt a bin harf as much fuss if that had a bin yar Granfar wot had a died instead o' the oul pig.'

My hart we ha' had sum feeds this week. Aunt Agatha gave us orl a luvley dinner o' pig's fry, grearvy an dumplins. Aunt Agatha she say you carn't mearke proper dumplins nowadays on account o' the flour – and she know.

Granfar he cut sum grub inter him, he had two helpins o' fry, he said that wus more like oul times. Arter dinner he gor inter the oul arm chair an slep tru the hull arternoon.

Aunt Agatha she dint eart no pork, she sed she dint fancy it, she say: 'That oul pig wus so friendly wen he wus alive that that wus a like a eartin one o' the fambly.' But o' corse she eart sum fry an soursages.

Oul Mrs.W— she cum in learter on (cos she heard we'ed killed the pig); she reconed she cum to borrow suffin, as Aunt Agatha say to me: 'John, bor, she borrer so much stuff orf o' me, I fear more at home in har house than I du my own.' Mrs.W— she kep a hummin and harrin to Granfar about his pig, but

20

he worn't a tearkin no hints, so larst o' orl she say to Granfar: 'Do you know the eleventh Commandment?' Granfar he say: 'Yis – I hard it years ago, thas, "Wen yow kill a pig send yar neybors a bit o' the fry" – but that dornt signify nowadays.'

Howsomever, my Aunt Agatha, who's very good natured, gave her sum scraps o' pork cheese an two soursages. Mrs.W— wus pleased, she went orf an forgot wot she cum to borrer. Fare yow well, together.——Yours obediently,

THE BOY JOHN.

PS.– Aunt Agatha she say she'd like to send yow an yar staff orl sum soursages, only she dornt know how many on yar there are, so she thort that would be better to send none, than send sum sum.

## ENJOYING THE FUNERAL

May 7th,1949.

Deer Sar – This here earnt a wery brite latter cus thas about a funeral. Granfar's oul pal Jimmie (you wunt know him), he's a darty oul man, he never hardly warsh, he ha bin an oul boozer, an he live all alone. Granfar use ter go an see him now an agin an allus took him suffin nice wot Aunt Agatha made for him. Granfar offered to clear away orl the cinders wot were piled up round his stove. He said, 'No, learve yow them were they are. I keep my feet warm on them.' He knew he wun't larst wery long, so he say to Granfar: 'You'll have a pint when I'm buried oun't ya'?' Granfar, to plearse him sed, 'Yis, we'll ha' one on the way back.' He say, 'No, ha yow one on the way there. I shorn't be wi' ya' on the way back.'

Well, in the finish they had to tearke him to the warkhouse (that earn't the proper name now). As soon as he got there they barthed him, blowed if he din't die a the same nite, yow see he worn't use ter bein' barthed.

Granfar went to the funeral, an' o' course Aunt Agatha went along o' him for company.

That oul Mrs.W— she wus there, as Granfar say, 'She din't orter a' went, she worn't asked.' She's one o' them wimen wot go to orl weddins and funerals (an auctions). She never go inter church. She jus' stan' agin the gearte, garp at everything, an tork about everybody.

I lay yow a shillin' yow country people ha' got one or tew like har in yar willage.

There was a sad accident at the funeral, oul Ben, our grearve digger, he tumbled inter the grearve, rite in front o' everybody (sum say he'd had a drop or tew ter keep his narves up). Well, wen they got him out they found he'd brook his arm. As Granfar sed, 'That feared to carst a gloom over the hull proceedings.'

Aunt Agatha she arsked Jimmie's sister, wot had cum a long way, inter tea (we had high tea) an' she got werry chatty wi' Granfar, an' wen she went he say, 'There ya' are, thas the most enjoyable funeral I ha' bin tew for a long time.'

Well, fare yow well together, so long.— Yours obediently,

THE BOY JOHN.

P.S.– Aunt Agatha, she say that earn't how long we live, tha's wot good we do do while we're alive wot count.


## AUNT AGATHA SPRING CLEANS

May 26th, 1949.

Deed Sar— I reckon yow wonder why I hearnt rit leartly. Well, Aunt Agatha she ha' bin a spring cleanin, an we ha' wery nigh finished, she ha' got only one more plearce to dew, thas outside (thas the coal shud).

Granfar he mob, he say yow carnt see no diffus wen thas dun, only yow carnt find northin. But he lend a hand. We got orl fit, wen Aunt Agatha found she'd lent har white-warsh brush to Mrs.W—, so I had to go arter that. Well bor she'd nearly slit that up. She say ter me, 'Thank yar Aunt Agatha for the use of tha brush. I ha gor a new one now so I shull neyther want to boorer nor yit lend.'

She ga' me sum peppermint cooshies for Granfar. He mobbed, he say, 'I dornt want them things, I only teark them wen I ha' got wind.'

Granfar boored a short ladder from the pub, he was gorne sum time. He cum back wi' a red fearce but Aunt Agatha never sed northin. Well we meard a statt. Me an Aunt Agatha did the front rume. Granfar sed he'd witewarsh the skullery, cos that ha' gor a low ceilin.

We got nicely statted, wen there cum a knock at the door. Aunt Agatha, she pearked true the kurtins, she say 'Blowed if that earnt the Wicar.' She say to Granfar, 'Dornt yow meark a' din, our Wicar is here, an yow arnt presentable.' She whipped orf har darty apron, arter she'd wiped har fearce, she put har hare rite, an answered the door.

The Wicar, he could see we wore in a muddle, she never arsked him in an he sed he couldn't stop, so he gan har har magazine, an orf he went.

We statted agin, but we couldn't hear Granfar, Aunt Agatha opened the skullery door, my hart there was a clatter. Granfar he feel asleep on the plank and wen she opened the door she tipped the hull lot over, but he wornt hart, his witewarsh pot wus broken (that wus cracked afore). Aunt Agatha she got a dwile, and wiped him down; he looked a jorb, that cum orf o' the top o' his hid best (he's borld). Howsomever we finished afore dark. Well, fare yer well tergether.— Yours obediently,

THE BOY JOHN.


P.S.– Aunt Agatha she hearnt got northin to say this week, she's tew busy.


## GRANFAR'S RABBITS

June 25th, 1949.

Deer Sar— Thas a gitten a rare jorb a riten to yow now, cos we're gittin busy on the farm, an I'm a warkin leart, a howin a sugar beet, an I wark hard cos I'm on tearkin wark. Then wen I learve orf I allus git sum rabbits' grub for Granfar (he keep rabbits). He nearly lorst sum the tother day. Aunt Agatha she herd a noise in the garden an blowed if there wernt an oul dorg arter Granfar's rabbits. She ran out; she hearnt northin else, so she took orf one o' har shoes and hulled at that oul dorg. The oul dorg picked up her shoe an away he went, an there wus my Aunt Agatha a hoppin about on one leg.

I gor unter my oul bike an went arter Aunt Agatha's shoe. I knew were that oul dorg lived.

O' course, oul Mrs.W— had cum while I was away, an Aunt Agatha set there wi' odd shoes on. She only cum acors she'd got on a new hat and new my Aunt Agatha hearn't seen it, thow she'd heard about it. She bort that new as soon as the chapel anniwersaries started. As Granfar say, 'She trearped rown to owl them anniwersaries, not because she's religious an yit to help the collections much, but just to show orf her new hat.' He say, 'Tha's a pritty hat, but har fearce spile it.'

She ha' just had the electric lite put in her cottage, so Aunt Agatha say to har: 'How do you git on wi' the electric lite, Mrs.W—?' She say: 'Tha's wonderful. The man finished larst Tharsday (an this is Satirday); he twitched it on afore he left and that hearnt gone out yit.' As Granfar say, 'She's sorft.'

Granfar he ha' bin moderate leartly; he ha' got the screws. He's allus wuss wen Aunt Agatha want him to dig sum new taters or chop sum kindlin, but he's allus better if he's a gorne a bowl playin. He hearnt played lately on account o' the cold. He say: 'Thas these weather forecast wot mearke it cold,' you know – 'Warm everywhere *except on the East Coast.*' Well fare yow well together for now.

THE BOY JOHN.


P.S.– Aunt Agatha say she's pleased my letters are appreciated. She say, if I can give sum people sum pleasure, well I'm a doin sum good in the warld.

# GRANFAR AT THE SHOW

August 1st, 1949.

Deer Sar— I statted (yis, I mean 'statted') to write ter you sum time back, only that wus so hot. Well, we orl went tew tha Norfick Show. Granfar's oul marster, wot he use ter wark for (an his farther afore 'em), he cum roun a tha Tharsday morning an took us orl in his motor. Granfar set in front. We went rite tru Norrich, rite parst yar orfice. I think you orl musta' gone to the Show, cus there wornt no one a lookin out a' yar winders.

We got there orl rite, an we had a rare oul jam roun. Then we dint see harf. Granfar, he got more tharsty a' tryin to git a harf pint then he would a bin if he hearnt a' had it. We took our dinners along o' us, an set under a grate oul tree. Granfar was suffin hot, so he took orf his sleeve weskit an set on that. Granfar could ha' had his dinner wi' our marster in a big tent, only Aunt Agatha she say, 'He use the nife too much to tearke anywhere.' Arter dinner Granfar he fell asleep, so Aunt Agatha she put a newspearper over his hid, and we went orf tew tha' flour show, an that wus luvley. Wen we cum back for Granfar, there he wus – gone.

Well, bor, we trearped about arter him. Larst o' orl we see him in a tent (where they sell beer). He was a' torkin tew a woman. She'd gor a glars o' stout and Granfar a half pint. We watched 'em; Granfar looked ever so happy till he cort site o' us. Then he went redder than ever, an he cum along. Aunt Agatha she say, 'Who's that woman you were a' torking tew?'

He say, 'Tha's one o' my oul sweethearts. I cum athort her nearme is Lysar. I new har wen she wus single. Har husbin is very moderate, an she say if anything shud happin to him could she cum an see me.'

Aunt Agatha she say, 'I'll give har "Lysar" if she set a fut over my troshall. An were's yar weskit?' We went back tew the oul tree, and there wus an oul dorg asleep on Granfar's weskit. He growled, but Aunt Agatha got him orf by givin him the rest o' our egg sandwitches. Arter that I'm blowed if that oul dorg dint foller us about the rest o' the day.

Well, thas orl fer now.— Yars obediently,

THE BOY JOHN.

P.S.– Aunt Agatha hearnt got northin to say, 'cos she's a coverin up the lookin glasses an a puttin the nives away 'cos there's a thunderstorm a cumin.

# HARVEST HOME

September 10th, 1949.

Deer Sar — I recon yow wonder where I ha' bin a gitten tew. Well, we ha' only just finished harvest. We had ter hull ourselves bodily intew it to finish a' the Tharsday nite.

Granfar he lent a hand, he led the hoss an halered 'Howjah'. Granfar say 'Wi' orl these new pearks to help em they dornt git the corn up so quick as we use tew.' Aunt Agatha she say 'Yow must remember Granfar, yow uster have pork an onion dumplins nearly every day. Nowadays about orl they git is spam an jam sandwiches, an no home brewed beer.'

Our marster (he's one o' the good oul sorts) gan us a rare good du a' tha' Saturday nite, wot he called a 'Harvest Home'. We cleared out one ind o' the oul barn, white warshed her, an the wimen they decorated it wi' flowers an flags. Old Mrs.W— she lent a hand, 'cos she knew she'd be arsked to the du then.

We had everything posh fa the feed, plenty o' home cured ham an proper sossages (I think a pig must a died on the farm aforehand).

We had little glarses of strong wine in front o' our pleartes to have afore dinner. Granfar he say 'I can't drink out o' them little tity glarses,' so they brort him a pint. Mrs.W— she drank his wine, as well as hars. Arter a real good meal, we had a sing song. Charley he brort his fiddel (wi' no strings on the bow). Jimmar, our milkman, he played his accordion, Granfar, he had a mow in. He sung 'Tom Bowlin', he got an uncore, so he sung it again.

Old Mrs.W—, she had a few, as well as Granfar's little glars. She did a sort o' a darnce to a tune called 'Knees up Mother Brown'. Aunt Agatha sed she wus disgustin. Granfar (with a werry red fearce) wanted har to do an uncore.

Well we finished a little arter eleven and orl sung 'Old Lang Zine'. That wus a jorb for sum on em, a gitten out over the oul barn troshall (about tew fut high). Old Mrs.W— she dint cock har leg high enuff to clear it. She fell flat o' her back outside. She lay there. Someone sed 'Git har a drop o' brandy.' Granfar say, 'Hull a pail o' warter over har; don't waste brandy.'

Howsomever she cum roun, an as Granfar say, 'A good time wus had by orl.' Well we ha' got a 'good pull' ahead on us – sugar beet – so fare ye well tergether.— Yours obediently,

THE BOY JOHN.

P.S.– Aunt Agatha, she say 'That earnt the hot weather wot mearke yer feel so hot; tha's a thinkin about it wot mearke yer fear wuss.'

# OLD MRS.W—'s OUTING

October 12th, 1949.

Deer Sar— You'll be pleased ter know our Old Folk's Club a hed an outin on the Broads, in a big motor larnch.

A lot o' people sent orl sorts o' things for dinner (Aunt Agatha called it lunch). We stopped an had that at St. Benet's Abbey. Granfar told us he could remember when there wus a cottage there near the river where they use ter sell porter to the wherrymen. Well, that wus suffin hot, so sum on em took orf ther shoes an socks an hung ther feet in the river. Aunt Agatha she say to Granfar: 'Dornt you tearke yars orf do you'll git rumatism.' She knew he hearnt warshed his feet (not leartly).

Aunt Agatha, she cleared up orl the pearpers we'd littered about, then orf we went roun Sowolsam an Ranner Broads then on to Hornin were we had tea in a big rume.

Old Mrs.W— who had warked har way inter this outin, she thort she'd be the furst one ashore. Well she shoved her leg out afore we were nigh enuff. Granfar, he pinned hold o' har other leg, dornt she'd a bin in, there she was, she looked a jorb, she straddled as far as ever she could, one leg on the shore, an Granfar a hangin on the other, larst o' orl har leg came orf the shore an inter the river. Granfar he hung on an saved har life.

She got one leg wet, so Aunt Agatha say 'tearke yar stocking orf Mrs.W—, that'll soon dry in the sun,' but she dint. Aunt Agatha knew why she dussent teark that orf in company. A cummen home we eat up orl the food what was left over. Mrs.W— she was a fuling about an showing orf, she set her fut right onter Granfar's big tom toe. My hart he hallered, an sed a bad ward (but that dint matter cos the Wicar dint hear him).

Granfar say to Mrs.W— 'You dint orter a' bin here at all, you wornt axed. You are alus a pokin yar nose (only he dint say nose) in where that earnt wantin. I wish I'd a let go o' yar leg at Hornin, we shud a had more rume in the larnch then, a cumin home.'

Well, as the old wherrymen use ter say in the old days when they sailed parst each other, 'Here wi' sail.' — Yars obediently,

THE BOY JOHN.


P.S.– Aunt Agatha, she say, that git late so sune a nights now, thas dark afore yow now where yow are.

# A MICHAELMAS SALE

October 29th, 1949.

Deer Sar— Aunt Agatha, she a bin away for a long week-end, so me and Granfar had to manage on our own. She went an kept house for sum people, wot she wus housekeeper for, for twenty-two year, an thas how she know how things should be dun proper in a house. She left us plenty to eart, you see, we hearnt finished a' earten our pig, not yit.

The furst day Granfar sed he'd go to the auction (he luv an auction), and cum back in time to git our dinner ridy.

Well, wen I got home he was sound asleep in his chair, there wus a sorspan on the tearble clorth, an the tearters had biled away. I thought to myself, 'If my Aunt Agatha could see this lot.' Well I wook him up, he feared fuddled and say, 'Wars up?' He say, 'Well John bor, I went to that there auction this mornin. I juss held up my stick to my pal Jimmar, to say how do, the auctioneer took it for a bid an knocked down a tarnip grinder to me for nineteen bob.

'I told the auctioneer I wornt a biddin (his name was George suffin). He see that wus a mistake, so he put it up again, and blowed if that dint mearke thurty one shilluns next time. The farmer wot that did belong tew, he cum roun an gan me half a crown, so me an Jimmar went an had a couple o' harf pints, so either that or the jamin about meard me tired.' Granfar he give me sixpence. I recon that wus so I dint tell Aunt Agatha.

Anyhow we had our dinner. That was orl rite, only Granfar forgot to put the sorlt in the tearters.

Old Mrs.W—, she poked her hid in to see if we wore a gittin on orl rite.

Granfar, he say: 'We are a managin orl rite thank yer, shut the garden gearte as yow go out.' She wanted Granfar to trim her roses. Aunt Agatha said: 'The only gardenin she really want you to do, Granfar, is to help to git rid o' her widder's weeds.' She know Granfar ha' got a bob or tew. Well I shall heter learve orf cos we're gort a hull lot o' warshin up to dew, so as we can have suffin to eart orf on tomorrer, so fare yer well tergether.— Yars obediently,

THE BOY JOHN.

P.S. – Granfar, he say, sorlt is wot meark tearters tearste narsty if yow dornt put it in.

## MRS.W— AND GUY FAWKES

November 12th, 1949.

Deer Sar— O' corse we had a bunfire; Granfar allus did ha' one. We searved up orl the oul hedge trimmins an' lumber, an' Aunt Agatha, she searved up orl yar pearpers (arter she cut out the 'Boy John' latters, 'Jonathan Mardle's' articles, an' any other Norfick peeces). We had it rite down a' yin ind o' the garden. Me an' sum more boys lit it, then my hart, dint that rain.

Aunt Agatha, she got inter the coalhouse an' watched, and Granfar got inter another plearce. Old Mrs.W— ask if we wanted any rubbish. Granfar say, 'Yis yow can bring that stuff wot yow sent to the rummidge sale an' they couldn't sell it.' Do you know, she cum to the bunfire (she knew Aunt Agatha allus hed tea and kearkes arterwards). Well she cum a-splatterin' athort our garden, rite tru Granfar's autumn lettices.

He mobbed a rummin. She cum rigged up for the weather, she looked a jorb wi' har umberalla up. Granfar say, 'Tha's a rummin she worn't shoved on the top o' sum bunfire afore she got here.' Well, she stood there a garpen at our bunfire, when a boy let orf a grate oul squib behind har; well bor, she jumped a mile, and fell rite inter a hole wot Granfar dig to put orl sorts o' rubbish in. Aunt new she must a hart harself, so she took har indoors an' wiped har stourkin, but she wunt teark it orf so Aunt Agatha could see wot she'd dun. Well, arter tea an kearkes she went home; Granfar lent har his stick (not his best one).

Nexter mornin' she went to the doctor's wi' a sprained ankle. Doctor, he had a look at it, he say, 'Less have a look at the other one.' She say, 'Oh doctor, I didn't come prepared for that.' Howsomever, she's better now; she wus wearin' a grate oul poppy wen she brort back Granfar's stick. He stay, 'I lay yow a shillun tha's one o' larst year's poppies, by the look on it.' Granfar say, 'There's two people in the warld I dorn't like – an' she's both on em.' Well I recon yow ha' heard enuff o' our troubles, so fare yer well tergether.– Yars obediently,

THE BOY JOHN.

P.S.– Aunt Agatha, she say troubles are like bearbies, the more yow narse 'em, the bigger they grow.

## GRANFAR AT THE POST OFFICE

December 6th, 1949.

Deer Sar— Granfar he ha' hed rumatism a rummin, an yit he allus carry a little tearter in his pokit, wus as hard as a stun now. He took nearly everything wot everybody told him, an then he got warse, so we hed the doctor. He say to Granfar: 'Have yow dun anything four it?' Granfar say: 'I ha' rubbed my leg wi' paraffin.' Doctor say: 'Thas a good idea, then you want to put a match tew it.' Howsomever, he sed he'd sen' Granfar a bottle o' medisen. Granfar say: 'Wen do I tearke it?' Doctor (who like a joke) he say: 'Yow tearke a dose o' that a quarter an hour afore yow feel the pains a cummin on.'

Well, he's better now, but he took so much stuff, he dorn't know wot did cure him. Anyhow, he wus well enuff to go to our Post Orfice a' tha' Friday for his pension.

O' corse, our Post Orfice earn't like yar Post Orfice in Noridge. Yars fear to me to be a grate big bilden, wot dorn't sell nothin only stamps an things, a proper wearst o' covered spearce. Our Post orfice sell everything an' anything, an' on a Friday arternoon yow can hardly sturrer, wot wi' oul earge pensioners, boxes o' fruit an' wegatables and hundreds o' odds an' inds.

Old Mrs.W—, she wus there, a fuleing about, an somehow she gan Granfar a little shuv, an' he bein bad on his pins, went over backards, an that fear he got his hinder part stick inter a box o' tomarters. Well bor, tew or tree on 'em got him up an arter sum time they got him outer that box. In the meantime, oul Mrs.W—, she cleared orf wi' out a waitin' for har pension.

Granfar, he mobbed a rummin, an' so did my Aunt Agatha when she cleaned his trousers down (they were his second best). Then she larfed. She say: 'Well, Granfar, that might a bin warse, if they'd a bin eggs instead o' tomarters,' she say. 'I knew yow were gorne to have a row when yow put yar new shews on the tearble a Tharsday mornin'.'

But, as I say, my Aunt Agatha is ever so goodnatured. She wunt hart a soul, why, she allus drown kittens in warm water, so they shorn't suffer. Well, fare yer well tergather.— Yars obediently,

THE BOY JOHN.

P.S.– Aunt Agatha, she say: 'That earn't wot yow look at, tha's wat yow see when yow do look.'

## GETTING RIDDY FOR CHRISTMAS

December 24th, 1949.

Deer Sar— We're hully busy a gittin' riddy for Xmas. Granfar he brort home a grate bunch o' Crissmas wot he'd gathered, but Aunt Agatha, she own't ha' that indoors afore Xmas Eve, she say that unlucker, so Granfar left it in the shud. Aunt Agatha, she ha' meard the pudden, we orl sturred it cept Granfar, she wunt let him, cos he had a cold in his hid. She sed she'd put sum rum in it, she say: 'I ha' got a little in the house, wot I keep in cearse none on us dint feel well.' Granfar he say to Aunt Agatha: 'I'm werry sorrer, but I dint feel well yisterday.' Well then she meard him go down to the pub to git sum more. He dint mind (but he was gorne sum time).

My Aunt Agatha, she's ever so kind, she ask Mrs.W— to cum an have Xmas dinner along o' us, cos she's orl alone (cept har cat). Aunt Agatha say to Granfar 'Dornt yow forgit to wish har a Happy Xmas.' Granfar he hummed and harred, then he say 'Orlrite, but I'm only gorn to wish har one.' Mrs.W— she's a funny woman, she got wrong a singin a' carols with the Chapel people, so she say to Aunt Agatha, 'I think I'll give up religion, I'm a gorne to leave Chapel and go to Church.'

She's about as sorft as Arny wot wark along o' me. He say to me yisterday mornin', 'Our marster say we ha' got to go a muck carten; one ha' got to fill, an one ha' got to lead; I'm a gorne to lead; what are yow gorne to du?'

Aunt Agatha she went to Norrich for har Xmas shoppin, she sed that wus orl a jorb, you could hardly sturrer for peeple, an yow couldn't git half wot yow wanted. She bort half a pound o' corfey; well, a cumin home on the bus everybody kep a saying they could smell corfey, so she sed she could tew, then they dint think she had the corfey. She bort sum miselto, my hart that wus deer. Granfar recon that'll wark out at about two bob a kiss. He wunt ha' that hung anywhere where oul Mrs.W— can catch him. He say, 'I dornt want har a slubberin over me.'

Well I must earse orf, an I wish yow an yar starf (espechally the one wot put this inter print) an orl yow wot read these latters a werry Happy Xmas. Yars obediently,

THE BOY JOHN.

P.S.– Aunt Agatha, she send har Best Wishes tew. She say thow she's a spinster, she earnt one o' the miserable type.

## A PARTY AT MRS.W—'s

January 28th,1950.

Deer Sar— Well, we got over Xmas orlrite. Aunt Agatha she never got that chicken wot Mrs.W— promised her for Xmas. Aunt Agatha say that must ha got better. Granfar he went to the plowen match 'er the Boxin Day. He had a go an won an ounce o' baccar, but he say that earnt like oul times, when the first prize wus a leg o' pork, an the hosses knew wot 'Kephere, Hait, Woosh' meant. That wus dark afore they finished, so the larst four furrers had to be plowed to a lanten. That wunt a bin tew bad, if sum siller fule hearnt a muved the lanten about when they wore a plowen .

Well, bor, them furrers looked a jorb nexter mornin. Granfar he cum home wi' a red fearce (they wore open orl day). He soon fell asleep in his chair. Aunt Agatha she wus annoyed becos orl larst week's pearpers, wot she wanted to look trew, wore underneath his cushion. When Granfar wook up he grumbled about a pain in his right leg. Aunt Agatha she say, 'Why, thas oul earge, Granfar.' He say, 'Oul earge be blowed, my other leg is just as oul, and that dornt hurt.'

Anyhow, Granfar rubbed sum oils on, not them white oils wot Boy Arrthur signified, but hoss oils; they're a lot stronger.

Oh, thank yer, Boy Arrthur an Wally, for yar latters about my latters; that dew gi' me a little hart o' grearse. Our marster (the editor) he recon as how there may be a book learter on, if I rite enow, an wen I're rit enow. Oh, we orl went down to Mrs.W—'s to tea a the nite arter Boxin nite. Granfar he dint want ter go; he kep a dwindlin about, but as Aunt Agatha say, that wus the proper thing to du. She say, 'She ha' bin to ours, so we ought to go to hars.'

Granfar he wus a eartin his second sossage roll (which he sed was werry moderate) wen Mrs.W— happened to say her cat died a tha Xmas Day. Well, bor, Granfar he slipped the rest o' that sossage roll inter his pocket (Aunt Agatha never see him) then he had sum mince pies to tearke the tearste away.

We ha a gearm o' cards. Mrs.W—, she won. Granfar sed she wunt a dun if she hearnt a chearted. A cumin home Granfar he wus sick. He sed he'd a bin orlrite if Mrs.W— hearnt a mentioned about ha cat a dyen when he was a eartin her sossage roll. Well, fare yer well tergather.— Yars obediently,

THE BOY JOHN.

P.S.– Aunt Agatha she say just becos we're a gorne to have an extra ounce o' bearcon, dornt buy a bigger frying pan – not yit.


### 'WOTE EARLY, AN GIT IT OVER'

February 22nd,1950.

Deer Sar— I wornt a gorne to rite northin' about what Granfar call 'this here blumin' oul election,' but that fear as if yow carnt help it. There's that oul Mrs.W—, bor she's full on it, every time she cum in she say to Aunt Agatha, 'Who dew yow think is a-gorne to git in?' But my Aunt Agatha she ount git led into it, she juss dornt say nothin'.

That Mrs.W—, she dornt know har own mine. She go to one meetin' an cum back and say, thas the one she's a gorne to wote for. Then another nite she go an hear the other side – then she dornt know wot to dew.

Granfar, he say to me, 'John bor, wen yow ha' wintered and summered as many elections as I have, yowl find them there people wot put up are orl alike (thow sum are batter then others).'

I meant to tell yow afore, oul Mrs.W—, she ha' got a new set o' teeth under this here naturalised healthy scheme – she look a jorb. She say the Govinment paid for 'em. Granfar, he say to har, 'Who is the Govinment?' 'Why, me an' Aunt Agatha,' he say. 'Wi' the tax on my beer an' bacca durin' the parst few year, I recon I ha' paid for yar top an' bottom set an' orl. Thank goodness every time yow open yar mouth I can see wot I ha' paid for.'

Granfar an' Aunt Agatha they git torken about pollitics. (Aunt Agatha she ownt argue – much). They were torken about Capital an' Learbor. Aunt Agatha she say, 'Yow dornt know the diffus.' Granfar say 'More dornt yow.' Well, they argered agin the nexter nite. Aunt Agatha say 'I'll tell you the diffus between Capital and Learbor if yow'll listen.' Granfar say 'Orlrite.' Aunt Agatha say, 'Now if I borrer five shilluns orf yow – thas Capital.' Granfar say 'Yis.' Aunt Agatha say, 'Well yow try an' git it back – thas Learbor.'

Granfar, he's suffin savage about that there law wot now stop his marster from a driven him to wote. Granfar say he ha' rid along o' our marster to wote at every election for as larst forty year (thow he knew Granfar dint wote the searme way as he did).

Well, we shull orl be glad wen this here blumin' election is over an yar pearper git back to normal, so wote early, an' git it over. –Yars obediently,

THE BOY JOHN.

P.S.– Aunt Agatha, she say, if yar pollitics are a gorne to stop yow from a doin' good deeds, well – dorn't give up the good deeds.


## MRS.W— AND THE ELECTION

March 4th, 1950.

Deer Sar— Well, thas over ( the election, I mean), an sum on 'em ha got wot they want – an sum hearnt. We dint fare to ha' no time to think about walentines nor yit pancearkes. My hart, that finished up a rumin, dint it? All them wot woted put down a X, that ment a draw – an they werry nigh got it tew, nigher than wot they git them football coupons.

Well bor, that wus a jorb the day arter the election, wen the results wore a cumin tru. Aunt Agatha, she statted a worshin up arter dinner, an she never finished afore tea time. She kep a learvin orf, a wipin har hans on har earpron and a riten down the results. Granfar he allus dooze orf arter dinner, but he dint that artemoon .

Old Mrs.W— she cum a pokeing a har nose in about four, she sed she couldn't hear down to hars cos har battery wus a runin down. Granfar say, 'Yow better ring up the B.B.C. an arsk them to tell the announcer to speark louder.'

Mrs.W— afore the election wunt tell us which way she woted, but arterwards she say to Aunt Agatha, 'Well, we got our man in.' Aunt Agatha knew she dint wote for the man wot won. Granfar say 'I'll find out which way she woted' (acors he's artful). He say to har, 'I lay you a shillun yow put yar X agin the middle one.' She say, 'Thas were yow are wrong. I put my wote agin the bottom one.' (Then we knew.)

Granfar told us about a farmer years ago (he wus a Tory). He told his steward Jimmur he's drive him to wote. Well, orl the day he kep a poken into Jimmur to wote Tory. They had several drinks an a good dinner (the farmer paid), an he felt sure Jimmur would wote Tory. Well, they woted, an on the way home he sed, 'Well Jimmur bor, we ha' hed a werry good time.' Jimmur sed, 'Yis marster, but we might as well a' stopped at home.' The farmer say, 'Wi how's that Jimmur?' Jimmur say, 'Well yow woted Tory an I woted Liberal, so we are where we were afore we went away.'

Granfar like yar arter the election pictures, only he say, 'Sum o' them wot lorst look happier than sum o' them wot won.' Well, as they say on the wireless, 'Here's to the nex time.' — Yars obediently,

THE BOY JOHN.

P.S.– Aunt Agatha she say, 'Yow dornt help people if yow do for them wot they should be a doin for their selves.'


## GRANFAR'S SCOTCH DUCKS

March 24th, 1950.

Dear Sar— Dorn't that fear a rumin yar pearper an my letters a-gorne rite to Americar. That'll be a jorb if me an yow help to searve the dollar situation. My Aunt Agatha, she say to me, 'Dorn't lose yar hid over that bit o' praise. Go to wark juss the same, and dorn't arsk for a rise (not yit).'

Oh, Granfar, he sold oul Mrs.W— sum ducks, they are four wot he got right away from Scotland. He dint tell har that Scotch ducks never lay a Sundays (she'll ha' ter find that out for harself). Wen he took the ducks Aunt Agatha she say, 'Dornt yow be long,' cos she knew oul Mrs.W— is sorter hangin' arter Granfar. Well, he wus gorne the best part o' sum time. Wen he cum back he sed he had to stop an' muve sum rabbit hutches for har. He say, 'She's as sorft as yow can mearke 'em, she ha' got a new hutch with a 5s. lock on the door, an' yit the door ha' got only leather jimmurs for hinges (proper Norrich fashion). A shuttin' nife wud soon git them rabbits out.'

Granfar he's a gardenin'. He has got his arly tearters in. He had a poor crop last year. He recon that wud a paid him to a let the garden a laid domino for a year.

Aunt Agatha she arsked Mrs.W— to tea a tha Sunday nite. Granfar he muttered a bit, but as my Aunt Agatha say, she lead a lonely life, an' my Aunt Agatha is ever so good natured. Mrs.W—, she allus drain har teacup now cos Aunt Agatha, she like a tellin' yar fortune, yow know, by tea leaves. She use' ter give Mrs.W— sum home truths, becos Aunt Agatha new more about har parst than she thort. We set roun' the fire arter tea. Granfar, he fell soun' asleep, an' soon began to snore, so Aunt Agatha tarned on the wireless. They were a singin' hymns, Mrs.W— sed she loved hymns (that wus only becos my Aunt Agatha is good livin').

Oh, Mrs.W— wus a grumblin' about har new teeth. She sed har top set wunt hold up. Granfar, he say, 'Yow want ter keep yar tongue up agin 'em, that'll hold 'em up.' She gan him a funny oul look, she knew wot he ment. Well, this ount du, I shull hetter hav a jam roun the garden, ther's plenta want doin' there, so fare yow well tergather.—Yars obediently.

THE BOY JOHN.

P.S.– Aunt Agatha, she say, 'Mrs.W— is allus aworryin' about suffin. She's one o' them wot worry, becos she ha' got nothin' to worry about.'


## AUNT AGATHA GOES TO NORWICH

April 15th, 1950.

Deer Sar— Well, Tombland Fair ha' bin an gon, an' Granfar he dint go to year, he fared a bit moderate, an' lorth to go, so me an' him got on wi' the garden. Aunt Agatha, she went a' the Saterday. She wunt a went, only oul Mrs.W— plearged har to go an help har to chuse a new coat. Aunt Agatha, acos she's good neartured, she went, but she say she'll never go to Norwich no more on a Saterday, not if she can help it. She say yow couldn't sturrer fer people and yow dint fear to git wot yow want.

Well they trearped about from shop to shop to try an git suffin wot ed fit. Orl the coats she fitted on looked orl rite till she did the bottom button up, and then they garped out at the bottom. Aunt Agatha say thas acos she's a gittin wide roun har hips. Arter they did buy a coat Mrs.W— took Aunt Agatha out to tea. That wornt so nice as where Aunt Agatha allus go; that wornt werry posh, an as Aunt Agatha say she do not like drinkin a tea outer thick cups (wi no sorcers). Mrs. W— she went on har own an bort a new hat (she wunt abort that perticlar hat if Aunt Agatha had bin along o' har).

Granfar, he new wot bus they wor a cumin home on, so he had meard tea for em, only he forgot to put the tea in the pot, so they had a good larf. (I new he went down to the pub a' the noontime, so I recon he wus a bit orf his gard.)

O' corse Aunt Agatha brot us sum fair buttons for tea. Arterwards oul Mrs. W— tried har new hat on; she looked a jorb. I thort Granfar wus a gorne to hav a fit. He say, 'I shud think that wud win first prize at any flower show.' Mrs. W—, she say, 'Well yow must ha suffin new on at Easter, else the crows will pick at yer.' Granfar say, 'Yis, an wurse an that, I shud think.' She went to church wi' har new hat on Easter Sunday (she hearnt bin for weeks). Granfar say, 'Next time she put that on will be wen she go to the chapel aniwersary at Whitsun – just to show orf.'

Aunt Agatha (out o' kindness) ask har to dinner Easter Sunday. O' course we had rubub an custard. Aunt Agatha, she ha' learnt Granfar to eart that now without mearkin a sloupin noise. Well, we shull hetter wait till arter Yarmouth Fair for the fine weather, so fare yer well tergether.— Yars obediently,

THE BOY JOHN.

P.S.– Aunt Agatha, she say the only ordinary people in our willages are them wot think they arnt.


## A WEDDING IN THE FAMILY

May 1st, 1950.

Deer Sar— We ha' hed a weddin' at ours. Granfar's grandorter got married this week, an Aunt Agatha sed to searve the expence o' hirin' a roum, they could hev it at ours. We'd dun our spring cleanin', so that wus orlrite. Aunt Agatha cleared out our front roum, took orl the likenesses orf the sideboard an the mantelpiece (as well as har two china dorgs). She took the auntermakassers oft her chairs, an' put away anything wot the kids mite muck about. Granfar lent a hand.

The weddin' party hed a car to go to church in, wi' white ribbands on; orl us others walked. They dint hev the car to cum back, acos that was hired for a funeral (afore the weddin' wus over) so we all walked back wi' the bride an' bridegroom in front. We cum a different way back so as we shunt meet the funeral. That wus a 'white' weddin' really, becos that snew a cummin back.

Wen we got home we had a rare good feed; there wus sossage rolls, beef patties, mince pies an' jellies, an' a special trifle. My Aunt Agatha she'd put suffin inter that wot hed got a kick in it. Aunt Agatha hed har best tea sarvice out (wot she only use for weddins an' funerals) an' wot only she warsh up. Old Mrs.W— lent a hand in the kitchen (Aunt Agatha paid har for that), but she kep' a putten harself forrid an' cummin tru inter our front roum, just as if she wus a guest.

She statted a pourin' the port wine inter the glarses, in the kitchen. Granfar he twigged there wus suffin wot wornt rite. He say to Aunt Agatha. 'Bring yow them bottles o' port inter the front roum an' yow pour them out; them glarses arnt above harf full wen they cum in here, and every time old Mrs.W— poke har fearce roun' the kitchen door that git redder than ever.'

We hed a good oul sing song arterwards. Our Wicar an' his wife cum in learter on, so the neybors couldn't say that that wornt a respectable du. They sung a duet wot meard us larf about 'A Hole in the Bucket.' Granfar sung his 'Tom Bowlen' (thas the only one he know). The bridegroom wus a gorne to sing 'A boy's best friend is his mother.' Granfar told him that wunt du, not there. Well everyone hed a rare good time, especially the children (tree on 'em were sick).

Wen Aunt Agatha went inter the kitchen to see how Mrs.W— wus a getting on wi' the warshen up, well, bor, that was only about harf dun, an' she set on a stule with har hid up agin the copper. She was farst asleep. Aunt Agatha said she must be werry tired. Granfar hed a look. He say: 'I ha weighed har up. I know wus a matter wi' har, she'll weark up afore she go home.' Well fare yer well agin tergether.— Yars obediently,

THE BOY JOHN.


P.S.– Aunt Agatha, she say, 'Wen yow weigh up people yow wanter watch not only wot they do, but also wot they dornt do.'


## GRANFAR AND THE WATERCRESS

May 20th, 1950.


Deer Sar— Poor Granfar, he ha' bin in the wars. That wus like this. Aunt Agatha, she's fond o' watercress. Granfar sed he'd git har sum for Sunday nite tea. She say: 'Dorn't yow git none out o' that oul deek wot run away from the back o' them two cottages, they hull everything inter that; git yow that cress outer the lan spring deek. I know tha's further to go, but tha's nice

36

runnin' warter there.' Well, orf went Granfar, wi' his frail barskit, an' a little oul garden rearke.

I wus a warken' in the garden, wen he cum back. Well, bor, I smelt him as soon as he cum tru the garden gearte.

I say: 'Granfar, yow ha' bin inter that stinken oul deek, where Aunt Agatha told yow not to go. He say: 'You are rite, John bor, but I ha' got a nice lot o' cress, an' you'll ha' to help me outer this muddle. I fell in when I wus a reachin' arter the larst lot.'

Well, I took him inter the shud. He say: 'Go yow indoors an' git yow me my secon' best trowsers, a dry pair o' socks, an' my high lows, they are clean.' (Yow see, Aunt Agatha she wus out.) Well, I warshed his trowsers an' socks in the warter tub, then I rinsed 'em an' I hung them back o' a little plearce down a the garden, so as Aunt Agatha shunt see 'em. Then I rinsed his cress in the searme tub, but they still feared to smell a bit.

Wen Aunt Agatha cum home she say: 'What a' yow dressed up for, Granfar? Where are yow a gorne?' He say: 'I'm a gorne a bowl playen.' (He suddenly thort o' that.) She say: 'Thort yow sed you'd got the screws.' He say: 'Tha's earsier now, an' I fear better.' So Granfar heter go orf to the bowlen green.

Aunt Agatha found out that there was suffin' wrong, wen she dint see Granfar's trowsers wot he took orf a hangin' on the back o' his bedroom chair. Well, then I had to tell her. Fust she feared annoyed, then she hed a good larf.

When Granfar cum home, Mrs. W— wus there. She new he'd bin arter sum watercress. He wus rite plearsed to give her harf wot he'd got, an' she was plearsed too. Well, we did have watercress for tea. Aunt Agatha's neybor brort har sum from Norwich a' tha' Sartiday. Granfar he wunt hev none; he dint know wot we wore a hevin' on wornt wot he got. He jus said: 'I fear to gorne orf watercress for a time.' Well, I shull heter knock orf agin, so fare yer well tergether.— Yars obediently,

THE BOY JOHN.

P.S.– Aunt Agatha she say: There's only one thing wuss than bein' torked about. Tha's not bein' torked about.

## GRANFAR GOES HOEING

June 28th, 1950.

Deer Sar— I reckon yow wonder why I hearnt rit leartly. Well bor, thas northen only, how, how, how. I're took on tew acres o' beet, tearkin wark, an if I can keep ahead o' them oul weeds, I can arn a bit.

Our wasse trouble is the oul mingins they hulley bite, towards nite. We set along side a fence tother nite, just haven a spell. Granfar was haven a draw wi' his pipe. Orl of a sudden he jumped up in a hurry an fell inter a holl full o' nettles.

I scrabbed him outer that. I say, 'Was the matter Granfar?' He say, 'Suffin now stung my leg a rummin.' We had a look. Blowed if that wornt an oul pishamare, he'd bin a setten on a pishamares' nearst. Well, he rubbed sum dock leaves on his nettle stings, and then, wen we got home, Aunt Agatha wus a puten sum bluenin on his pishamare bite wen in cum oul Mrs.W—. Granfar he hallered an' told her to keep outside for a time. He dint want har to see his leg. (He dint mind Aunt Agatha.)

Mrs.W— cum to see if Granfar wud go down to hars. She sed, 'Larst nite I cleaned out my rain tubs; we had a lot o' rain larst nite, but wen I looked this mornin' there wornt a drop in the tub; an oul sparrer hed built up the spout, so will yow please cum down an shoot the sparrer.'

Granfar say, 'Dornt tork so sorft wa's the good o' that. I'll cum down an' clean the spout out agin the nex shower cum.' He went learter on (wen he knew she was out).

Granfar, he went wi' the Old Folk's big outen to Yarmouth. Mr. King, that gentleman from Norwich wot go round to the Old Folk's Clubs, had told them about the outen sum time back, so they hed orl searved up. Granfar, he kep along o' his chummies, acos oul Mrs.W— kep a hangen arter him.

Wen they got home Granfar an his pal Billur went an' hed a half-pint apiece. A feller in the pub wot cum from London wus mearkin a gearme of country peeple, an' torkin about country fules. Granfar say to him, 'If you want to find a fule in the country, well, you'll heter bring him with yer.' Well, thas earsed orf a rainin', so heres orf again.— Yars obediently,

THE BOY JOHN.

P.S.– Aunt Agatha, she say, 'Many a woman has lorst a good sweetheart by a marryin' on him.'


## GRANFAR AT THE SHOW

July 15th, 1950.

Deer Sar— Well, we orl went to the Royal Norfolk Show, in Royal Norfolk weather. Granfar's oul marster took us in his motor. Granfar set in front. We driv rite up to where yow go in, becos our marster he wus a member. Arter we got in, we split up. Granfar went along o' our marster, an' me an' Aunt Agatha went orf to the flower show; that wus luvely, only that wus suffin hot in there (that was a' tha Thursday).

We hed a good look roun', an' then dint see a corter on it. We sed as how we'd meet Granfar at harf arter twalve, outside a sartain stand. Well arter a bit he an' our marster cum out o' there. Granfar's fearce was red. He sed that wus becos that wus hot in there. Aunt Agatha smiled, she knew.

Our marster went orf to hev his lunch, an' we hed our dinner, wot Aunt Agatha brort with us, under a greart old tree. We hed a Thermos o' tea, and Aunt Agatha brort proper cups. Granfar dint hev no tea, he sed he wornt dry.

Arter dinner Granfar set wi' his back agin the tree and doozed orf so Aunt Agatha put a newspearper over his hid, an' we went an' hed another look roun'.

We see a long que' for the lunch tent an' blowed if oul Mrs. W— wornt at the ind on it. She looked a jorb. She'd got har heavy black dress on, an' har anniwersary hat. Bor she wus orl of a muckwarsh. She must a seen us an' slipped inter that que' just for swank, becos we could see she'd got har dinner in har net bag.

Well, we watched har, wen she thort we wore outer site, then she walked outer that que'. Yow see she wus jealous acos we cum in a motor car, an' she cum in a bus along o' orl them others.

We picked Granfar up agin, an' hed a look at the farm machinery. We saw a lot o' new fearks, wot Granfar dint understand, but he dint git tired a looken at them beautiful hosses, but wot pleased us most of orl wus a seein' the King and Queen an' Princess Margarate. They cum ever so close to us, they looked luvely, an' ever so homely. Granfar took his hat orf (Aunt Agatha dint hev to tell him); as Aunt Agatha say, 'People wot live in London orl their life ha' got to stan' for hours, an' then never git the chance to see our Royal family so close up as we hev.'

On the way home we had a drink at Fearkenham. Granfar met one o' his oul pals wot hed bin to the Show tew. Well, bor, they did sum howen an' a mowen for about a corter o' an hour. He asked Granfar wot he thort o' the Show. Granfar say, 'Well, I never see so many blumin wheels a gorn roun' in orl my life.'

Well, fare yer well tergatha.— Yars obediently,

THE BOY JOHN.

P.S.– Aunt Agatha, she say, 'Things look bad, but keep a smilen; tha's more infectious than the flu.'

# HEIGHAM WATER FROLIC

August 28th, 1950.

Deer Sar— I recon yow ha' bin a wonderen wot wus up acors I hearnt rit leartly. Well bor, we are up to our necks now, I mean wi' tha harvest, an if that hearnt a bin for a tempest a stoppen on us, I shunt a rit yit. Thas a jorb a cutten to year, tha' oul barley lay orl ways. The farmer nex to us, he's orlrite, he ha got enow thistles in his barley to keep it from a layen. Granfar he ha' bin a lenden a han.

Oh, Granfar he hed a day out larst Tharsday week. Our marster's son, wot went away to the Shears years ago, he cum over here for a holiday. He took Granfar to Potter Heigham Regatta (wot Granfar say they use to call 'Heyam Worter Frolic').

He had a rare good time, especially wen sum young leardies axed him into their yot (Aunt Agatha she'd rigged him up so he looked tidy). He hed a glars o' beer, an some cearkes along on them, an plenty to say. Wen he left they say to Granfar: 'We are pleased to meet yer. We hope you'll see more on us nex year.'

Granfar say: 'Well if I dew, yowll git locked up, becos yow hearnt got tew many clothes on now.' They larfed.

Arter that, Granfar he went to the Fair, an then he stopped to see the fireworks, an he never got home till eleven o'clock. Aunt Agatha she looked at him an she say: 'My word, the sun ha' got hold a' yow.' He say, 'Yis', an went straight orf to bed.

We wore orl took to the St. Benet sarvice on the Bank Holiday Sunday. That wus werry nice, an the Bishop spoke so nice an homely, Granfar could understand every word. I'll tell you wot plearsed Granfar a rummin tew – just afore the sarvice the wherry Albion went a sailen parst, just like oul times Granfar sed, only he was sorry his oul pal Bob Hewitt wornt aboard.

Oul Mrs.W—, she wus there. She slipped up alongside a Granfar an started a torken to him during the sarvice. Granfar he shushed har, acos he know how to behearve, if she dornt.

After the sarvice sum young fellars orf a yot tried to teark a rise out o' Granfar. They say to him (just becos he looked old): 'Have yow ever seen any monks about here?' Granfar say: 'Only in the summer time.' They say: 'What real monks?' Granfar say: 'Monks? I thought yow said monkeys.'

Well, fare yer well tergather. Here's orf to bed to git fit for the mornen.
— Yars obediently,

THE BOY JOHN.


P.S.– Aunt Agatha, she say: 'You profit by experience, when you meark a mistake (the *second* time).'

# GRANFAR AT THE FETE

September 9th, 1950.

Deer Sar— Yow will be plearsed to know we ha' got trew harvest orlrite, so I can git my second wind now fit for the oul sugar beet agin. We hed a garden feet in our willage, on the Wicar's lorn, an' my hart they meard sum money, nearly a hundred poun. As Granfar say: 'The hull lot on 'em (includen the Wicar) dint look worth five pouns.' We orl lent a hand a gitten things ridy ('cept oul Mrs.W—, an' she never cum nigh nor by).

There wus orl the different storls, an' orl sorts o' gearmes – hoop lar, treasure hunt, sticken the tail on the dicker an' bowlen for a pig. Granfar he hed a go at the bowlen, but he meard rather a moderate hand on it. Oul Mrs.W— she hed a go tew, only she chearted; she hed one more borl then she shud a hed, an' wen she hulled har larst borl she hit the chap wot was a picken on up. He warnt werry plearsed.

I hed tew or tree ice crearms. Granfar he hed one tew. Aunt Agatha hed to trim him up a bit arterwards, 'cos yow see he ha' got whiskers.

There wus a bit of a disturbance during the arternoon, that wus like this. There wus a pail o' worter wi' a shillun in the bottom, an' if yow could drop a penny on the shillun, yow could hev it. Oul Mrs.W— was a hevin a go at this, wen sum boys wot were a fulen about gan har a shuv behind. Well bor, she went plump inter that pail o' worter. Granfar wus near by, he helped to pick har up, then blowed if she dint tell him that wus him wot shuved har. My hart he was suffin savige, she mobbed Granfar an' she say to him. 'If yow wus my husbin I'd mix yow up a doose o' pysin.' Granfar say, 'Yis, an' if I wus yar husbin, I'd teark it.'

Aunt Agatha, who wus a helpen on a storl, she cum up an' parted 'em, an' the Wicar's wife took oul Mrs.W— inter the Wicarage, rubbed har down, an' gan har a cup o' tea an' the Wicar got another pail o' worter. They couldn't find the shillun anywhere. Granfar say, 'I know who ha' got that shillun, an' a cup o' tea for northin as well, but I aren't a gorn to mention no nearmes.'

Then there wus sum more trouble; the pig got out. He got inter the Wicar's garden, an' fell into a darty oul hole where they put muck an' rubbish, so we hed to warsh him down (we dint teark him inter the Wicarage). Well, we finished orf searme as we allus dew wi' 'kissen in the ring.' Oul Mrs.W— she meard a drive to git Granfar, but the Wicar's wife got Granfar furst. He wus plearsed; he dint want that oul Mrs.W— imitaten to kiss him. Well fare yer well agin tergerther. — Yars obediently,

THE BOY JOHN.

P.S.– Aunt Agatha, she say, 'Tha's no good a putten yar fut down if yow hearnt got a leg to stan' on.'

# THE VILLAGE FLOWER SHOW

October 7th, 1950.

Deer Sar— We shud a hed a proper Flower Show in our willage only that fell trew, acos they couldn't git a proper tent. Well, we thort as how we'd have a small one on our own so we formed a committer. There wuss the Wicar, our schulemaster, a gardener, a small-holder, my Aunt Agatha an' another leardy. The lanlord at our pub, he lent 'em his club rume, an there wornt no drinks to be sarved in there, so that wuss kept respectable. Well, bor, they got sum stuff togethar, cos ours is only a tity little willage, an' that wuss only flowers an' wegetables. Granfar, he wuss down there orl the mornin', a riggen up the tearbles an' tressels, an' gittin things riddy.

He cum home to dinner wi' a rare red fearce. He say to Aunt Agatha, 'That wuss a hot job a gittin that rume riddy.' She just looked at him an' sed, 'Yis.' Granfar he hed his dinner, then went orf sound asleep in his chair. Aunt Agatha smiled an' sed, 'He's tired out, John.'

Well, the show wuss a great success, there wuss a hull scalder on 'em there, an' a hull lot o' stuff. Aunt Agatha she had arranged the flowers, an' they looked luvely. Old Mrs.W— she showed sum onions; well Granfar knew she never grew none. They meard sum enquiries an' found out she'd bought sum big uns at the shop on the corner. O' course she wuss disqualified an' one o' the committer mobbed har a rummin. She wuss proper upset an' cleared orf inter the tap rume, an she dint cum back till after sum time.

Learter on the Wicar, he wuss mearkin a speech, oul Mrs.W— wuss a leernin on up agin the wegetable tearble, wen the hull lot went over, har an' orl. Well, bor, that wus a jorb for a time, there wuss tomarters, tearters an' onions a rollen about orl over the rume, an' the grate oul wegetable marrer wot the Wicar grow rolled orf an' knocked over a little tearble wi' orl the flowers on, an' there was oul Mrs.W— a layin' on the floor among the broken dishes an' squashed tomarters. They got har up, an' she wuss as white as a sheet. Someone sed, 'Git har a drop o' brandy.' Granfar say, 'Give yow har a glass o' warter, that'll newtralise things a bit. I can smell har breath from here.' My Aunt Agatha gan him a funny oul look.

Well, that wuss a jorb a putten things rite agin; that wuss a good jorb the stuff hed bin judged afore, cos nune o' the tearters went back unto their proper plearts. Granfar wuss savidge wi' that oul Mrs.W—, cos he won farst prize wi' his tearters, an' he felt rite proud wen people kep' a readen his red farst prize ticket wi' his nearme on. Well, tha's that, so fare yer well tergether.— Yars obediently,

THE BOY JOHN.

P.S.– Aunt Agatha, she say, 'Aluss teark a pride in yarself. If yow are poor, dornt look poor.'

42

# MRS.W— MOVES OUT

October 20th, 1950.

Deer Sar— We ha' bin busy, leartly. Oul Mrs.W— she ha' muved out o' her cottage inter a row o' housen futher away from ours. We orl lent a hand. Granfar an orl, acos he wus plearsed she wornt a gorn to live so nigh ours. O' course in Norwich yar Micklemas day is a September the 29th, well we hev ours on October the 11th – the proper day.

The Monday afore Micklemas day someone asked Granfar where Mrs.W— lived, he say: 'Go yow down to yin ind o' this rud, till yow git nearly down to the tarnpike. On yar rite yow'll see a double dweller cottage wi' tew lots a warshen a hangen out. Hars 'ill be the warshen wot look as if that want doin agin.'

Me an' Aunt Agatha went down. Granfar he drawed down learter on. Our marster he sent his man an' a hoss an' waggon. They wanted Granfar to help an git the things from upstairs. He sed: 'No, I arn't a gorne to hev peeple mearken a gearme o' me, a loaden up things outer the bedroom.' (Cos as yow may guess there's allus a lot on 'em a garpen to see wot they can see when anyone is a muven.)

Well, bor, she'd got sum oul lumber. Thas a good jorb there wuss a good breeze, 'cos that blew the muck outer har farniture. Granfar he wuss a carrying a pail full of preserved eggs unto the waggon. He say to me: 'I wonder where they cum from, John. She dorn't keep hins and she dorn't buy eggs. I lay yow a shillun our oul hins will lay better wen she git down to her new cottage.'

Granfar he go to lift up her rabbit hutch, wen the hull bottom fell out, an' the rabbits orl ran about in the garden. Well bor, we stowed 'em up at larst. Mrs.W— she mobbed Granfar, she sed he did it a parpas. He lorst his tamper, he say: 'Dorn't tork so sorft, that hutch is like everything else you ha' got, yow an' orl, thas rotten. I cum to lend yow a hand an' thas orl I git for it. I'm orf home.' Aunt Agatha see he wus upset, she say: 'Go yow home, Granfar, an' git the kittle a bilin, we shorn't be long.'

Well, wen that oul waggon wuss loaded up, that looked a jorb. Oul Mrs.W— she set on top, har hat wus tied on wi' a wrapper, an' she wuss a narsen har cat; me an' Aunt Agatha walked behind.

Granfar wuss a leanin on his garden geart wen they went by. He shouted out: 'Ha the elephants gorne parst yit?' Well bor, I thort as how she wuss a gorne to hull har oul cat at him.

Aunt Agatha she say: 'Cum yow indoors, Granfar, an' for goodness seark learve orf scratchen. Go yow an' hev a good warsh an' a chearnge, time I git tea ridy.' Well, fare yer well tergather.— Yars obediently,

THE BOY JOHN.


P.S.– Aunt Agatha, she say: 'She's a werry wise woman wot say nothen, at the right time.'

# GRANFAR AND THE SUGAR BEET

December 9th, 1950.

Deer Sar— I hearnt rit yow leartly, a cos as the boy say, 'There hearnt bin nothen to rite home about.' That fear nothen only sugar beet nowadays, wi' sluss up to yar neck.

If sum o' them, in warkshops in Norwich, wus asked to lend us a hand an see the sort o' wark we're a doin on, well bor, they'd strike afore they statted. Now we are bunged up wi' snow, farst that snew, then that blew an then that friss, so now we arnt a doin nothen. That fear a rummin how they tarn them darty oul sugar beet inter beautiful white sugar, but they du, dornt they? My Aunt Agatha, she can bile them a certain way till they mearke syrup, wot she mearke cearkes with.

Granfar, he lent a hand, only he went an catched a cold, an hed a bad corf. Oul Mrs.W— herd about it, an she brought him sum corf mixture, just afore tea time, so Aunt Agatha hed to ask her to tea (so Granfar only had one kipper). Nexter mornen Aunt Agatha say, 'Yow are a corfin better this mornen, Granfar.' He say, 'So I ort, I ha' bin a corfin orl nite.' She say, 'How'd that corf mixture tearst?' Granfar say, 'Tearst! I never tearsted it: I rubbed it on my chist, an that wornt half stickey.'

He's better now, an Aunt Agatha hed to git on his track; you see, he'd borrowed Mrs.W—'s barrer to muve his chicken shud outer yin ind o' tha' pightle, up alongside the house, so we could hear if anyone wus a pinchen our chickens.

Well, the bottom fell out of the barrer (that wus broke), Granfar he wus a' nailen the bottom in a tha Sunday mornen. My hart, my Aunt Agatha went arter him, she say, 'Whatever are yow a thinken on, mearken orl that noise on a Sunday?' He say: 'Well, that old fule want har barrer back farst thing a Monday mornen.' Aunt Agatha say: 'Well, if you must mend it today, put screws in, not nails.'

Mrs.W— brort her sister down to ours tother nite; she's werry similar to Mrs.W—, only har husben is still alive. She say to Granfar: 'You know, I'm worried becos I dornt know where my husband git tew a nights.' Granfar say: 'Yow'd be a darned site more worried if yow did know.' Well, things arnt a looken werry bright, wot wi' the unsettledness an everthing yow want to buy being hained. There fear northen to look forrard tew. As Aunt Agatha say: 'When the war wus on there wus peace to look forrard tew.' Well, fare yow well agin. I'll rite agin afore Christrnas.— Yars obediently,

THE BOY JOHN.

P.S.– Aunt Agatha, she says: 'Poverty earnt no disgrace, but that can be werry inconvenient.'

# AN OLD-FASHIONED WINTER

December 23rd, 1950.

Deer Sar— Granfar hearnt sed once this week, 'We dornt git them old-fashioned winters like we use tew.' He was up arly a' tha' Satiday mornen, an shovelled a parth to the coal shud, an another plearce. Then a boy cum an sed as how Mrs.W—'s pump was friz up. Aunt Agatha say, 'Yow'd better go down, Granfar, an see wot yow can du.' Well bor, he hummed an hard. Aunt Agatha say, 'Go on Granfar, yow want to hev sum o' the Xmas spirit in yow now.' He say, 'Yow'r rite, so I do, an I like rum best.'

Well, he went down. She biled sum warter, an Granfar soon got the oul pump a gorne. She arsked Granfar to cum in an hev a cup o' tea. He sed, 'No thank yer.' (He wornt a gorne inter har house alone in kearse the neybors wud tork.) Howsomever, she brort him out a cup o' tea, but he poured that inter the snow wen she wornt a looken.

Oh, afore I forgit, Granfar he went round wi' tha carol singers; he dornt sing (not outside), he carried the hurrican lanten, but o' course he dint stay out as leart as them there others. They hed a good time at our marsters (they allus du). He arsked them inter his kitchen, where they hed tea, sossige rolls and mince pies.

Wen we orl cum out agin, oul Mrs.W— picked up Granfar's lanten, wot he'd left outside the door. She say, 'Here yow are, Granfar. I'll tarn the wick up for ya!' Blowed if she dint tarn it the wrong way, an orl the wick went inter the bottom o' tha lanten. Granfar wholly mobbed har, an told har she shunt a' meddled with it, and he meard har teark har hat pin outer har hat an there was him an har a fishen that wick up outer that lanten. Wot annoyed him wus, wen they wor arter that lamp wick, oul Mrs.W— say, 'My ward, I can smell rum.' Granfar gan her a funny oul black look (wi' his red fearce) .

Well, thas a jorb to know wot to hev extra for Xmas to year. We are hevin a cockrel, wot Granfar fattened up, as Granfar say, 'Years ago everybody hed a joint o' beef, or else a greart oul lump o' pork for Xmas. This year we look like a hevin a bloomin site more musted than meart on our pleartes; but there yow are, we shull heter du the best we can, but that fear a rummin dornt it, the more civilised we fear to git, the less grub we fear to hev.'

But Aunt Agatha she say we shall manage, we allus did, there's a lot o' people warse orf than us, an we can allus enjoy a nice cup o' tea. We're orlrite for tea, acos Aunt Agatha ha' got a friend wot dornt drink tea (yow'll understand). Well, afore I learve orf me an Aunt Agatha, an Granfar, wish you a Werry Happy Xmas, yow an yar Starf tew, an orl them wot read this an orl. Yars obediently,

THE BOY JOHN.

P.S.– Aunt Agatha, she say: She's werry glad she worn't born afore tea wus inwented.

# HOW GRANFAR HAD THE 'FLU

January 27th, 1951.

Deer Sar— We copped it. Yis, the 'flu I mean, the hull lot on us, and I ken tell yow who gan it tew us, that wuss that oul Mrs.W—. She cum to ours larst Monday week to show Aunt Agatha har new shews wot she'd bort up in Norridge. Well bor, she'd got a churchyard corf on har, an she kep a corfen a rummen. Aunt Agatha say to har: 'Put yar hand in front o' yar mouth wen yow corf, don't yow'll hev them jarms orl over the house.' Well, she undid them new shews an stood em on the tearble. My hart, Granfar he twigged them, an he walked them orf on the floor wi' his stick. He say: 'We dornt want no rows in this house,' but there wuss one straight away.

As soon as she went Aunt Agatha say: 'She ha' got the 'flu orlrite.' Granfar say: 'Flu! By the way she's a carryen on, an by how she's a splarren out har feet, she ha' got the fowl pest, an there's only one cure for that.' She hearnt bin gone tew minutes afore Granfar statted a sniffen, so Aunt Agatha meard him barth his feet in hot musted an water, gan him the rest of our Christmas rum an sent him orf to bed.

Well, we orl knew we hed got it nexter mornen, but Aunt Agatha, she kep about. She say: 'A woman will allus keep a doin, where a man will give up.' Aunt Agatha wont hev the doctor in. She say too many people teark advantage o' this so-called free medical sarvice, and the poor doctors are overwarked.

She hed har own home cure for us – plenty o' biled onions an opened medecen. Granfar's pal Jimmur herd were orl layed up, so he cum roun an lent a hand, choped sum kindlen' got in the coal, an warter. Jimmur say he never did hev a cold, an that acos he allus keep a bunch o' onions in his bed. Aunt Agatha say: 'Thas no wonder yow never got married, Jimmur.'

Of course, yow know, in our williages, no body dornt really want for northen. If anyone is ill, or want any help, well, someone is soon roun there, an my Aunt Agatha earnt one o' the larst. Bless har hart. Our marster sent us a load o' firewood, an a harf bottle o' port for Aunt Agatha an a harf bottle o' rum for Granfar. (He never statted a gitten better till that rum wuss finished.)

Old Mrs.W— she nither cum ny nor by. Granfar say: 'An a good jorb tew, a spreaden har jarms orl over the plearce. She's nither use nor ornament.' Aunt Agatha say: 'Yow shunt tork like that, Granfar.' He say: 'Well, she meark yer.' Well, tha's a rum jorb a riten wen yow ha' harf got the 'flu. Anyhow, we are orl a gitten on, so fare yer well tergether.— Yars obediently,

THE BOY JOHN.

P.S.– Aunt Agatha, she say: '"Pay as yow go" is a good motter, an if you cant pay, well dornt go.'

# SHROVE TUESDAY

February 8th, 1951.

Deer Sar— That was a' tha' Shrove Tuesday, an we'd bin a troshen an finished about harf arter twalve. Wen I got home Aunt Agatha hed gone to Norridge, to buy sum things, afore they riss any more. Granfar he set alongside a' tha' fire wi' a red fearce, an full o' fulery. I found out that arter he an Jimmur cum an hed a look at us a troshen they hed a harf pint or tew on the way home.

Granfar torked about other Shrove Tuesdays, wen they allus hed a plowen match for a leg o' pork. He say 'Yow dornt see a leg o' pork nowadays, only wen you look inter a pigsty (then there ha' got to be a pig in it.) Granfar say 'Look here, John, yar Aunt ownt be home afore four; shall we try an meark sum pancearks? We ha' got the stuff in the house an we oughter manage atween us.'

I got sum flour an milk an eggs an starred it orl up in a bearsen. Granfar found a fryenpan wot hed a nice lot o' fat in. He held that over the fire an I poured my stuff in. Granfar say 'We'll du one an try it; that shall be a "tearster".' We both lent a hand a' tarnen on it over arter one side was dun, but that dint look a bit like a pancearke wen that wus dun.

We harfed it an he say 'How du yars tearst, John?' I say 'Mine tearst fishy.' He say 'So du mine, an smell fishy tew. I tell yow wot we ha' dun, we ha' used yar Aunt's fish pan.' An so we hed, but we eart it up; we wornt a'gorn to wearst it. I found the other fryenpan (that wus nice an clean), put sum fat in, an we got a'gorn agin. The trouble wus that wud stick to the pan, an we hed a jorb a tarnen on 'em over, they would roll up.

We wore a heven our forth panceark and Granfar wus a looken out o' the winder. He say 'My hart alive, look wus a cumen up a' our garden parth!' That wus old Mrs.W—. We hed to arsk har in. She say 'Oh, yow are a' mearken pancearks!' (o' course everything stood about.) She say 'I'll du one for yow, an toss it tew. I're tossed hundreds.'

Well, Granfar drawed his chair up alongside a' tha' fire an wus a unlearcen his shews (acos his feet wore unearsy) just wen she wus a tossen the panceark. Blowed if she dint miss an harf that panceark fell unto the back o' Granfar's neck. My hart he sed a bad word an jumped up, an I thort he wus a'gorn to hit har. Bor, she shot out o' our house quicker than she ever went out afore.

Well, Granfar sed things about har wot yow dusent put inter print. His neck wornt barnt an I wiped the grearse orf. We wore a hevin' our larst panceark wen Aunt Agatha cum home. She stood a looken, she could see what we'd bin a doin'. She say 'Well, you hearn't brook northen?' We say 'No.' Then she looked roun' agin an hed a rare good larf. So, fare yer well agin.—

Yars obediently,

THE BOY JOHN.

P.S.– Aunt Agatha, she say, 'Yar pearper is worth tuppence if only for reporting calamities – such as deaths an marriages.'

# GRANFAR'S VALENTINE

February 22nd, 1951.

Deer Sar— Well, tha's orl over, sugar beeten I mean, the larst load went away a Tharsday. Bor, we never warked in so much mud an sluss afore in orl our lives. Oh, did yow ha' yar tea by daylite the furst Sunday arter Walenten? We allus du in the country. Granfar, he got a Walenten card, that cum by the furst post, that was orl 'I luv yow. Yow are my sweethart an my Walenten,' wi' a lot o' kisses an harts on it. He wornt werry plearsed; he thort by the wryten that oul Mrs.W— hed sent that. As I ha' told yow afore, she sorter hang arter him. He say, 'Lot o oul squit; hull it on the fire.' Aunt Agatha say 'No,' an she stood it on our mantel peace.

Oul Mrs.W— she called in a tha' forenoon: she hardly got indoors afore she sed, 'Oh, I see yow ha' hed a Walenten card, Granfar.' (We new then she'd sent it.) He say, 'Yis, sum fule must a sent it. Pity they hearnt got northen better to du.' Acors, we orl got Walentens at nite. They statted a lumpen on our door about harf arter seven. Furst cum an ounce o' baccer for Granfar, then two mittens for me (I'd seen my Aunt Agatha a nitten them). Arter that there cum a tin o' pork for Aunt Agatha (we sent that). Acors, the larst lot wot cum wus the brume a fallen in; we new that wus the finish. Aunt Agatha wus plearsed wi' har tin o' pork. She say that'll help our meart ration. She say, 'Larst week we must a' hed a peace o' Rudolph the red-nose Raindeer.' Granfar say, 'Yis, an nex week I reckon we shul git a bit o' Puddy Tat' (he listen to the wireless). The funny thing wus, we'd gan Jimmur our Walentens to send, an Aunt Agatha hed gan him hars to send. We found that out learter on.

Oh this shud amuse yow. Granfar allus warsh his feet a' Satidy nites an Aunt Agatha allus git things fit for him. Well, she wus a gorne to Norridge on the Satidy, an not a cumen home afore the larst bus, so he hed to warsh his feet a' tha' Friday nite. Well, a' tha' Satiday mornen, blowed if he dint cum downstairs dressed up in his Sunday best. Aunt Agatha say, 'Wot are yow a gorne out, Granfar? Wot ha' yow got yar best clothes on today for?' He say, 'Well, this is Sunday, earnt it?' She say, 'This earnt Sunday, this is Satiday mornen.'

Well, bor, he garped, then thort, then statted to larf, then we orl larfed. He say, 'I thort that was a rumen, wen yow hearnt laid out my Sunday things, an I ha' still got my weekday shart on. I recon that orl cum about tru a warshen my feet a tha' Friday nite stead o' tha' Satiday.

Well, accorden to yar pearper, about this here Z business, I look like being called up arter harvest. Well, that ount be warse than a' sugar beeten. Granfar recon that hed there bin another letter in the alfabet he'd a heter a gone. Well, so long, tergather.— Yars obediently,

THE BOY JOHN.

P.S.– Aunt Agatha, she say: 'Reality, is wen yow leave dirty dishes in the sink, and they are there wen yow git home.'

# THE PIG KILLING

March 13th, 1951.

Deer Sar— Now I recon this'll meark yar mouth warter. Larst Tharsder, we hed pigs fry an' dumplens, wi' rare nice grearvy (an' we are only poor peeple). Granfar say, 'I recon this is our "Festival" dinner, John.' I'll tell yow suffen else, we ha' got sum proper sossages (not harf breard), so I know we shull hev sossage rolls for tea a' tha Sunday nite, an' we ha' got sum pork cheeses an' scraps (I like them). Well, I'll tell yow how we cum by orl that luvely grub. Granfar's pal Jimmur killed a pig in ter house, an' we orl went down to lend a hand. Aunt Agatha, she wus a cutten the stuff up, I wus fetchen an' bilen warter an duen. Granfar he wus a grinden out the sossages, wen there wus a knock on the door.

Aunt Agatha wipe har hans on har earpron an went, an blowed if that wornt oul Mrs.W—, she recon she wanted to see Aunt Agatha about suffen. Granfar say 'She know you ha' killed a pig, Jimmur, she's arter wot she can git. If she cum trew here, I'll shuv har trew this sossage masheen.' (We wore a warken trew in Jimmur's back plearse.) Howsumever she went orf, an learter on Aunt Agatha took har a pork cheese sum pigs fry, an sum scraps. Granfar say, 'I dornt suppus yow meark much outer the pig Jimmur?' He say, 'No, but I mussent grumble, you see I ha' hed the company o' the pig orl winter, and I ha got the muck now he's gorne.' Granfar say, 'Yar pig dint weigh as much as I thort it would, an I never thort it would neither.'

A few days learter Mrs.W— sent ward down to say as how she wornt well. Aunt Agatha went to hars, an foun har a bed. She sed she thort the scraps hed upset har, but wot she hed got wus a rare bad cold. Well my Aunt Agatha werry near spring clearned that house as soon as she got there, then she see to Mrs.W—. She put orl clean things on the bed an warshed a nitedress in cearse she hed to call the doctor in. Aunt Agatha sed she wus a bad pearshant. She say to Mrs.W—, 'Will yow hev sum beef tea?' She say, 'No, thankyer.' Then she say, 'Well, will yow hev sum nice brorth?' She say, 'No, thankyer.' Larst o' orl Aunt Agatha say, 'Well, will yow hev a drop o' hot rum?' She sed, 'Yis plearse, meark it strong an meark me teark it.'

Aunt Agatha say, wen she cum home the other nite, that Mrs.W— was much better, only she can't git much sleep. She told har as how she hearnt closed har eyes orl nite. Granfar say, 'Well how du she recon she'd a gorne to git to sleep if she dornt shut har eyes?' Fare you well agin tergerther.— Yours obediently,

THE BOY JOHN.

P. S.– Aunt Agatha, she say, 'If you are married a wife is there if you want her.' Granfar say, 'Yis, so she is if you *dornt*.'

# GRANFAR AND THE CENSUS

April 14th, 1951.

Deer Sar— I recon yow wunder where I're bin a gitten tew leartly. Well, I hearn't felt a bit like ryten, wark on the farm this winter ha' bin enuff to breark the hart o' marster an' man. We hearn't even got our oats in yit, an' as Granfar say, 'Cuckoo oats aren't no good.' (I recon you'll soon be gitten sum 'furst to hear the cuckoo' latters.)

Oh, I must tell yow, about harf arter five larst Sunday nite oul Mrs.W— drawed inter ours. Granfar say to har, 'Ha yow hed yar tea?' She say, 'No I hearn't.' He say, 'Pity, we ha hed ours.' She reconed she dint feel up to a site, har house feared to be lonely an' got on har narves, an' she say to Aunt Agatha, 'I wunder if yow could put me up, juss for the nite, I're brort my nitedress.' Granfar gan har a funny oul look but Aunt Agatha sed, 'Orl rite my dear, tha's a rainen like anything, we'll manage yow somehow.' Then Aunt Agatha gan har sum tea.

Arterwards we set there a torken. Granfar say to har, 'Ha yow filled up yar senses pearper?' Mrs.W— say, 'No, I hearn't, I're got it here wi' me.' He say, 'Wi tha's no blumen good if yow are a gorn to sleep here. I thort I cud smell a rat wen yow cum in tha' door. Yow must ha' cum down a parpus to sleep here, do yow wun't a brort yar nitedress wi' yow,' he say, 'Yow ha' landed me in for a nice oul job, I'm hid o' this house, an' yow'll cum on our pearper now.'

Well, we got the pearper out (o' course, Aunt Agatha did the ryten). Granfar arst har sum lot o' questions, a lot on 'em wot worn't on the form at all. Mrs.W— say: 'Well, surely they dorn't want to know orl that?' Granfar say, 'If you are a gorn to argur, yow can teark yar senses pearper, an' yar nitedress, slip orf home, an' fill it up yarself.'

She dint tell Granfar her rite earge. He say, 'If you are only as oul as yow say, yow shun't be a tearken tha' oul earge pension not yit,' but my Aunt Agatha put that rite, acos she new. Then agin, she reconed she'd only bin a widder once. Granfar say he new she'd buried at least tew on em. She say to Granfar, 'Yow better put me down for a barth room, that look better.' He say, 'Barthrume! The only barthrume yow ha' got hang up on a nail in yar washouse.'

Well, arter Granfar hed finished wi' har, Aunt Agatha gan har har supper an' she went to bed, an' we filled up our parts o' the senses pearper, wot we dint want her to know about. Oh, we are orl plearsed about the Budget news, wi' the rise in the oul earge pensions, but as Granfar say, 'We ha' got to live till October afore we start a gitten on it.' Well, fare yow well, tergether.— Yars obediently,

THE BOY JOHN.

P.S.– Aunt Agatha, she say, 'A man can be a fule an' not know it – but not if he's married.'

# GRANFAR SWEEPS THE CHIMNEY

April 28th, 1951.

Deer Sar— We ha' bin a gitten on like an oul house a fire on our farm leartly, wi' the nice fine weather, but tha's orl a jorb. Yow see, our marster, he plan a long way ahid wot he's a gorn to sow in each piece, only the wet weather a stopped orl that. We hed to put oats in where there shud ha' bin wheart, an' agin barley in wot shud ha' bin o' wheart, so yow see tha's upset everything planned for nex' year as well as this. We ha' got to plan a year ahid. O' course, yow town people wunt understand this (thow sum on yer wood).

Well, Aunt Agatha she ha' statted spring cleanen, an' the plearce earnt a bit like home, thow I know that'll be nice wen she ha' finished. She wanted the chimley swept. Granfar say, 'If the boy John will lend me a hand, we can do that an' searve the sweep. I ha' dun scores.' Well, arter I left orf I borred our marster's long ladder, put it up to the chimley an' helped Granfar to rig up his idea. We got a long bit o' line, Granfar he'd bin inter tha' oul plantan an' cut a branch orf a holly bush, an' tied that inter the middle o' the line, then he tied a brick unter the holly branch to help the weight. Well, I got up atop an' dropped the line down a' tha chimley to Granfar, so Granfar pulled down an' I pulled up.

Aunt Agatha she'd cleared har china dawgs an' clock orf o' har mantelpiece, an' put two sheets up in front o' tha' fire plearce. Granfar, wi' sum rite oul trousers an' a slop on, warked behind this sheet. Oul Mrs.W— she heard wot wus a gorn on, she cum an' hed a look. Acos she wanted har chimley dun. She wus a pearken trew the top just where the sheets dint quite meet to see wot Granfar wus a doin' on. Well, rite then the blumen brick fell down a' tha' chimley. Well, bor, the soot cum out inter the rume, and so did Granfar. He wus as black as a nigger an' he wus a chooken, an' wen he cort site o' oul Mrs.W—'s fearce (that wus as black as his) he larfed as well as corfed, an' Aunt Agatha hed to clap his back to searve his life. Wen he got his second wind he say to Mrs.W— 'Tha's wot yow git a sticken yar nose in were that earnt wanted' (only he dint say nose).

Well, that wus sum time afore Aunt Agatha got things rite agin, includen Mrs.W—. Granfar say to Mrs.W— 'Are yow a gorn to hev another peark afore I finish?' She say, 'No, I arnt such a fule as I look.' Granfar say, 'No, yow aren't.' (She dint know quite how to teark that). Arterwards, Aunt Agatha say to me, 'We shall hev the proper sweep nex' year John.' Well, fare yer well, together.— Yars obediently,

THE BOY JOHN.

P.S.– Aunt Agatha, she say: 'All husbands are alike, only they have different faces so you can tell 'em apart.'

# GARDENING AND LUMBAGO

May 19th, 1951.

Deer Sar— They ha' both on 'em copped it – Granfar an Aunt Agatha (the lumbeargo, I mean). That wus orl dun a tryen to du tew much in the garden at one time, wen we hed that short fine spell, acos, like everyone else, we're orl ahind hand. Aunt Agatha say, 'I shall hev to keep a douen, that'll wear orf.' Granfar say he'll try an wark his orf. He hed a spell o' tew in the garden Whit Monday, then he went an leened on our front garden geart, to sorter git his second wind. He say to Aunt Agatha, 'You know a leernen on that geart, I nottus the peeple wot are packed inter them little oul cars look as happy as can be, an yit them peeple wot drive in them big posh cars ha' nearly orl on 'em ha' got fearces as long as fiddles.' Bor, Granfar he's rite, du yow nuttis nex time you'r out.

Old Mrs.W— she cum to ours a' tha Whit-Sunday nite. Granfar see har a cumen up o' our garden parth. He say, 'She's onley a cumen here ter show orf; she ha' got a new rig out on, she look a jorb!' She'd bin to our Chapel Anniwersary tha' wus held in our marster's barn. She sed the barn wornt decorated so well ter year, there wornt no labarnam, yit no lilack. (o' course, that earnt out not yit.) Well, she'd got on one o' har oul hats, wot hed bin dun up wi' new feathers, an a coat wot stuck out where that shunt stick out. Aunt Agatha say she know the leardy wot that use to belong tew. Mrs.W— bort that at a rumidge searl – but not in our willage.

Mrs.W— sed as how har brother hed dug har garden, an knocked his self up, so she wanted sumone to help har to git har seeds in. She said on the packets that said they shud a bin in in April. Granfar he never imiteated to orfer to go. He say to har, 'Thas no use a payen regard ter wot that say on them packets, yow carn't "farm agin the weather".'

Aunt Agatha she went down a' tha' Whit-Monday to Mrs.W—'s and Granfar say to me arter dinner, 'Yow better go down an lend yar Aunt a hand, John, an git that oul gal's garden dun.'

You know, thow Granfar's a trifle orkard at times, he ha' got a hart o' gold' – he really think the warld o' my Aunt Agatha (an me). Granfar, learter on, had a jam down as far as his pal Jimmur's. They wore in Jimmur's garden, an o' corse his garden look a jorb, cos he earnt no gardener. Granfar he looked round, he say, 'If I wus yow, Jimmur, I shud let yar shooten ter year.' Well, I hope I ha' putt the rite stamp on this letter, these here new colors are messen us up proper. Well, fare yer well, tergerther.— Yars obediently,

THE BOY JOHN.

P.S.– Aunt Agatha, she say, 'Be careful about gossipen, becos them wot gossip with yow will gossip about yow.'

# MRS. W— SEES THE PRINCESS

June 23rd, 1951.

Deer Sar— No suner we fear to finish, we fear to statt agin (the oul sugar beet I mean); that dornt fear long since I rit an' told yow as how we'd dun, dew it? Granfar he lend a hand, acos I ha' took on tew eacres, tha's so much an eacre for a howen. If yow ride about the country yow can tell the diffus atween them wot are on tearken wark an' them wot wark by the day, acos if there's a spot or tew o' rain them on day wark will learve orf and shelter; if they're on tearken wark, they put on ther jackets an' keep a duin.

Oh larst Monday, Aunt Agatha went to Norridge to see the Princess, oul Mrs. W— she'd plearged har to teark har, acos oul Mrs. W— hearnt never seen no Royalty. Well they went orf on the farst bus a tha' mornen, afore we got yar pearper tellen on yer wot times to be in different plearces to see.

Well, that wus hot on the bus, so wen they got orf Mrs. W— sed she was suffen dry, so Aunt Agatha took har to a shop an' she hed a big bottle o' pop, an' then they stood two hours in the crowd. Mrs. W— took har dinner along o' har in case they couldn't git northen; she hed sum bred an' butter an' sum tomarters in a pearper bag. Juss wen the Princess was a gorn parst, the crowd shuved forrard, an' oul Mrs. W— she dropped har dinner, an' blowed if she wornt a proggen about arter har tomarters, instead o' looken at wot she cum to see.

So she lorst har dinner, an' naver see the Princess till she got parst. But she did git'a good vew learter on. Well, Aunt Agatha took har out to dinner, but as Aunt Agatha say, she dornt know har tearble manners. She sloup wen she eat har custed with har spune; even Granfar dornt mearke a noise when he's a usen a spune (not in company, anyhow). Wen Mrs. W— got back home, she say to Granfar, 'I see the Princess a setten alongside a' the King, in a car; she looked luvely.' Granfar say, 'Dornt tork so sorft; that wornt the King, that wus the Lord Mayor of Norridge.' O' corse Granfar hed bin a readen yar 'Evenen News' what Aunt Agatha hed brort home, with sum good pictures in. Granfar call 'em gays.

Aunt Agatha said wen she saw the streets orl lined wi' people, an' the street orl empty, that would ha' bin a rare chance for 'Jonathan Mardle' (wot like a walken down the middle o' the road) to hev a go; she sed, tew, that the perlice wore werry kind, and the crowd werry good. Well, fare yer tergether. Yars obediently,

THE BOY JOHN.

P.S.– Aunt Agatha, she say, 'Yow can mearke many a false step by standen still.'

53

# MRS.W— HAS AN OUTING

August 4th, 1951.

Deer Sar— I hope yow ount mob me for not haven ritten leartly, but we ha bin ever so busy, a gitten a' tha' hay up and a howen the beet, an the oul beet look well consideren, so now we're a' brushen a' fences an cleanen out the holls.

That wus werry nice a yow, Mr. Editor, to call an see me wen yow wore round our way; that wus a rumen how yow twigged me in my warken clothes, acos the larst time I see yow wus in yar orfices, an o' corse I wus trimmed up then.

Tha's a pity yow dint hev time to call an see Aunt Agatha, she would ha' bin plearsed, an she would ha' gan yow a jar o' har home meard rarsberry jam, an I know she'd a meard yow hed a glars a' har parsnip wine .

Oul Mrs.W— she cum down to ours tother mornen to borrer sum jam jars. She's bin a plucken a gousberries for a neybor, an wus a gorne to meark sum gousberry jam. Granfar say, 'I wonder how she cum by har gousberries, acos she hearnt got a bush in har garden.' Aunt Agatha lent har six jars (they wore clean). Granfar say to Aunt Agatha, 'Yow fear as if you'll du anything for anyone.' She say, 'Yis Granfar. I'll du anyone a han's tar, acos every time I du I allus feel a cumfortable feelen inside.'

Mrs.W— cum next mornen an brort Aunt Agatha ajar o' har gousberry jam (Granfar wunt ha' none). She told Aunt Agatha she'd bin a warken hard leartly, so she thort she'd hev a outen, an arter dinner she'd go to a funeral in the nex willage. Well bor, she called at ours, about harf arter one, orl dressed in black wi' a new skart on (new to har). She looked a jorb, an that wus suffen hot. Granfar say, 'By the time she ha' walked them tree miles, in orl this heart, she'll fear fit for har own funeral.'

Well bor, she cum back arter tea, she wus proper dun up. Aunt Agatha meard har sum tea; she sed she'd had a nice time, an hed a rare oul gossip along o' sum more women, yow country peeple know who I mean. There's sum in every willage, an they allus stan outside the churchyard geart at orl weddins an funerals. Well, that tempest ha' warked away over Norwich, so I'll git to wark agin, a' brushen. So once agin, fare yer well tergether.—

Yours obediently,

THE BOY JOHN.

P.S.– Aunt Agatha, she say: 'Marriage is a fine institution – for them wot like institutions.'

# ARTER HARVEST

September 17th, 1951.

Deer Sar— We ha' dun – Harvest, I mean – tha' oul barley wus a jorb. Sum on it wus fit, an' sum on it wornt. Granfar lent a hand a' pitchen a' barley. He wore his slop, acos them oul barley hams would ha' stuck to his gansey a rumen.

Granfar say Harvest earnt like that use to be, there earnt no 'go' in it. Years ago wen they hed to mow orl the corn, an' tie it up by hand, they got Harvest dun a lot quicker than wot they du now wi' orl their new fearks to help 'em. He say agin, 'Young fellars nowadays dornt know wot wark is. Only larst week a' tha latter part o' tha artemoon, wi' tha sun a shinen, there wus a hull lode on 'em a gorne up to Norridge to tha Speedways (or tha Dawgs), an' our marster's wheart stood there a arsken to be carted. Tha' rained orl the nexter day so that wheart wornt carted afore tree days learter.' Oh, wen yow city and town people ride trew tha country yow'll notis our stacks arnt so big this year; tha's acos the straw earnt so long, as Granfar say, 'There earnt a lot a boke ter year.'

Oul Mrs.W— ha' bin in tha wars agin. She cum inter ours, about half arter seven. Har fearce was red an' har hair looked ruff; she plopped inter a chair, an' asked Aunt Agatha for a peppermint sweet, acos she'd got 'digestion. Aunt Agatha gan her tew, an' she doosed orf in a chair. ,

Granfar cum in learter on; she set there sound asleep. He say, 'Was up wi' har?' (She set there sound asleep wi' har mouth wide open, she looked a jorb.) Aunt Agatha say, 'She ha' hed indigestion an' she asked me for a peppermint sweet to cure it. I ha' gan her tew.' Granfar, he smelt a rat, he say, 'Indigestion! wa' the oul fule is drunk. I cud smell gin halfway upper tha garden parth. Teark har outside an' I'll hull a pail o' warter over har; that'll put har rite.'

My Aunt Agatha wus annoyed, she shook har, an' wook har, she jumped up harf frightened an' that fear as if har hairpins cort in the arntermacasser on the back o' tha chair an' that cum away wen she got up, an' she looked a site wi' that a hangen on har hid. (Granfar got up and walked out.) Aunt Agatha gan har a torken tew, then meard har a strong cup o' tea. She sed she'd bin inter the nexter willage to see har new friend wot she'd met at a funeral sum time back; they went inter a little back rume in a pub an' hed tew gins each.

As Aunt Agatha say, 'Mrs.W— fear to love a funeral.' A short time back she wus a watchen one go by, an' she wus savage acos she wornt asked (especially wen she heard wot a luvely tea they hed). She say to Aunt Agatha, as they went by, 'If anything should happen to me, I shunt ask none o' them to my funeral.'

O' course my Aunt Agatha know har manners just like a leardy. If there's a funeral a-gorne parst ours, she go an' show har respects by standen at the garden geart, not pullen the kartens a one side an' pearken trew like a lot on 'em dew.

Well fare yer well tergether agin.— Yars obediently,

THE BOY JOHN.

P.S.– Aunt Agatha say, 'Never hit a man when he's down – he might git up agin.'

## THE HARVEST FROLIC

October 6th, 1951.

Deer Sar— We hed our Harvest Thanksgiven Sarvice larst Tharsday nite. The church wus butefully decorated wi' corn, flowers, fruit an wegetables. Aunt Agatha hed helped with the flowers. We orl went; Aunt Agatha took Mrs.W— tew (Granfar never set nex to har). Wen we cum out Aunt Agatha say to Mrs.W—, 'Wot a splendid Sarvice, an wot a luvely sarmon.' Mrs.W— say, 'Yis, but I dornt think the onions an tearters wore as big as larst year.'

We hed a rare du a' tha' Satiday nite. Our marster gan a Harvest Home (wot Granfar call a Harvest Frolic). We cleaned the oul barn down an whitewarshed her. Granfar lent a hand, an wen we hung the flags up an decorated wi' corn and flowers, bor that oul barn looked a treart. We had proper electric lite to year; our marster ran that athort the yard from the house.

We hed a luvely feed. Granfar say, northen like that use to be, wen they allus hed beef an plum pudden, an plenty on it. Oul Mrs.W— wus there. She wornt inwited. She was paid to help to sarve, an warsh up, an she soon meard an exhibition o' harself. That feared as if suffen went wrong wi' the lites; they went out, then they suddenly cum on agin. There wus oul Mrs.W— a moppen someone's beer down; o' corse everyone larfed, but my Aunt Agatha wus annoyed an Granfar wus suffen savidge.

Arter dinner we got tha' oul fiddle an tha' concerteenar a gorne, then we hed a sing-song. Granfar sung 'Tom Bowlen'; he got an uncore so he sung it agin. We finished up wi' 'kissen in the ring'. Oul Mrs.W— wanted to join in that, but my Aunt Agatha told har that wornt har plearce so she kep on wi' har warshen up. Granfar he hed a go, an blowed if the Wicar's wife dint choose Granfar, an she kissed him an orl. My hart, Granfar wus suffen plearsed.

We finished about harf arter ten. Juss afore we cum away our marster corled us a one side. He gan Granfar a drop o' rum. Aunt Agatha a glars o' port, an me a bottle o' pop. Wen we got home Aunt Agatha thort about Mrs.W—, acos she should a cum wi' us. I got unter my bike an went down to Mrs.W—'s. There wornt no lite, an har key still hung on the back o' tha' shud door.

Aunt Agatha wus properly worried, so me an har went back to our marster's. He say, 'Thas a rummen; surely tha oul fule arnt still in the barn.' Well, he got a lantern, we unlocked the barn, an hunted high an low, then larst o' orl we found har sound asleep on sum corn secks wot we'd put up a' tha' corner; har false teeth lay alongside on her. We wook har up an she fear dearzed, but she cum tew arter a time. Aunt Agatha picked har false teeth up and put them in har hankerchief, an arter a time we got her over the barn door troshell.

Closh, our hid teamman, he wanted to push har home in the wheel barrer. Aunt Agatha sed: 'No, that ount do; me and John'll manage.' We got har home orl rite an Aunt Agatha put har to bed. Wen we got back we foun Granfar sound asleep in tha' chair. We dussent tell him nourthen, so Aunt Agatha put har handkerchief inter soak an went to bed. Well, fare yow well agin tergether. Yars obediently,

THE BOY JOHN.

P.S.– Aunt Agatha, she say, 'Widows arn't the only ones who have late husbands.'

## GRANFAR'S POLITICS

October 22nd, 1951.

Deer Sar— We're a gitten on like an oul house afire wi' tha oul sugar beet; that spell o' fine weathar helped us a rumen, an' gan us a good statt. The beet arnt quite so big ter year (not our way) an' they're a bit fangey. Our marster say tha's acos we hed saveral wet spells, so they din't heter go down arter the moisture, then agin, o' corse, they hed a leart statt.

Well, as Granfar say, 'We ha' got another blumen oul election a cumen.' He's more moderate now wi' his ideas than wen he wus younger. He say one side can't be orl rite an' tother side orl wrong. He say to Aunt Agatha, 'They dorn't want an election, they want a "selection" an' select the best men on both sides, tha's common sense.' Aunt Agatha say, 'Yis, Granfar, you're rite, but yow must remember, common sense earn't so common.'

Oul Mrs.W— go a trearpen about to orl the meetens round about, an' yit she earnt't none the wiser. She allus think the spearkers wot ken tork ever so quick, an' shout ever so loud, an' keep a lumpen' on the tearble, are tha ones to vote for. As Granfar say, he ha' noticed tearn't orfen them wot tork a lot are any good for wark, an' yow ginerally git one on a farm.

Aunt Agatha say, 'I can't understand why Mrs. W— go to orl these political meetens.' Granfar say, 'I can; tha's acos they're free, anything free an' she'll hev it. Look at har spectacles, she dint rearly want 'em. She see a darned site more than she shud do without them, an' she naver wear 'em. Then agin, har false teeth, she only put them in wen she's a gorne anywhere particular (then she teark 'em out to eart with). Anything free she's arter it. If the Govinment wus to issue free prams, she'd ha' one.'

Mrs. W— got upset at a meeten in our sculerume. That feared as if Bob's oul sow got out unto the rud; sum on 'em wore a driven on her back. The sculerume door wus open, on account the heat, an' blowed if tha' oul sow din't bolt in. She tried to git unind a form wot Mrs. W— an' sum more wimen wore a setten on; over went the form, wimen an' orl. Well, there wus a commotion: Wimen a shreeken, an' men a halloren. Arter a time they got that oul sow out an' picked the wimen up. No one worn't hart, only Mrs. W— lorst har hat. Aunt Agatha say that worn't werry serious, acos she ha' got a lot o' hats; she allus buy one or tew at rummage searls (but not in har own willage).

Aunt Agatha allus go an' hear both sides. She say they orl tell yow wot they're a gorne to du if they git in. None on 'em tell yow wot they're a gorne to du if they dorn't git in. O' corse, Aunt Agatha will have a tork to Mrs. W— afore she wote. Like Granfar, Mrs. W— allus tearks nutis o' wot my Aunt Agatha say.

Well, as I sed afore, 'Wote early an' git it over.' So fare yer well til arter the election.— Yars obediently,

THE BOY JOHN.

P.S.– Aunt Agatha, she say, 'Yow can do wot yow want, if yow dorn't think yow carn't.'

## AUNT AGATHA'S ADVICE ON COURTING

December 10th, 1951.

Deer Sar— Well, tha' blumen Election ha' cum an gon, but them there oul sugar beet fear to go on for aver; we keep a' pullen an a' norken, we keep a' duin in orl sorts a wather; as Granfar say, 'We shull git dun sum time.' Oh, Granfar he's werry consarned about this fut-an-mouth disease. He say wi' orl this high edgercaretion they ha got nowadays, they orter be earble to cure that by now. He say years ago they never uster kill, they uster cure 'em, wi' plenty o' stockhome tar an salt. Any fule ken kill; they want to cure' em.

Oh, I muss tell yow about Jimmur a' tha' Election day. He went an woted arter tea, an there wus a young fellar outside tha' scule geart – he wus a' checken. He say to Jimmur 'Who are yow a woten for Jimmur?' Jimmur say, 'Ah!' an he went an woted. Wen he cum out this fellar say, 'Tell us who yow woted for, Jimmur.' Jimmur say, 'Well, ken yow keep a secret?' He say 'Yis.' Jimmur say, 'So can I. Goodnite.'

Oul Mrs.W— she ha' bin integearen wi things wot dornt consarn har. That wus like this. I happened to be a walken along o' a young woman a' tha' Sunday arternoon. Har nearme is Jessar (yow wunt know har). I wus only out wi' har juss for a parstime. We wore a gorne parst oul Mrs.W—'s. I see har a pearken out o' har winder (acors she dornt miss northen). Well, she must ha' gon strait down to my Aunt Agatha's an told har. I heard arterwards as how she went down there to borrer a book. O'corse that wus har excuse. She went down full on it, about the Boy John had statted courten.

Thaas a good job my Aunt Agatha dint ask har to ours to tea; I'd ha' gan har suffen to git on with. Well, wen I got home to tea, I knew there wus suffen on, acoss Aunt Agatha she sorter kep a' smilen, an Granfar gan me sum comical oul sly looks. Arter tea Aunt Agatha say, 'They tell me yow ha' statted courten, John.' Well bor, I wus flabbergarsted. I know my fearce tarned red, an Granfar he set there a' grinnen like a cat. I thort to myself I know who told them, thas that oul Mrs.W—. I see har a tarnen inter har geart wen I wus a' cumen back (alone). Aunt Agatha wus werry nise about it acoss she know Jessar is a nice young woman.

Aunt Agatha say, 'If aver yow start a' writen luv letters, be careful. I'll tell yow what happened to me once. I'd been a few weeks in service an I wus friendly with a young man in the nex willage. I set down an rit to him about meeten me wen I cum out o' church on Sunday nite. I rit another letter to my mother, an blowed if I dint git them into the wrong envelopes. So, John, if you write letters, allus seal one up afore yow statt on another.' Well, fare yer well together, till Xmas.— Yars obediently,

THE BOY JOHN.

P.S.– Aunt Agatha, she say: 'Some men git what they deserve, others remain single.'

## CHRISTMAS AT HOME

December 29th, 1951.

Deer Sar— Well, we got trew Xmas orlrite, an hed a werry nice time. Aunt Agatha arst Mrs.W— to ours for Xmas Day. Granfar wornt werry pleased, but, as Aunt Agatha say, 'The poor oul soul hearnt got nowhere else to go.' Granfar say, 'Thas a pity.' Granfar seft up an bought Jonathan Mardle's book for a

59

Xmas box for Aunt Agatha, an she read that to him a' nights. Aunt Agatha gan Granfar a pair o' mittens, an me two socks (wot she knitted). Oul Mrs.W— brort us a two pound jar o' har home meard jam (Granfar wont ha' none).

We hed a rare good dinner, an the tearble wus laid out proper. My Aunt Agatha wus brort up wi' good families, an know how things shud be done. Wen she go an keep house up at the farm, she allus teark orf har earpron afore she anser the phone. Well, we dint want much tea, thow Aunt Agatha got har best tea sarvice out (wot we allus use for funerals and weddens). Arter tea oul Mrs.W— meard a fule o' harself, she put a great lump o' our home meard tuffey inter har mouth, well bor I thort she'd a chooked harself. Aunt Agatha took her tru inter our scullery, an them tew managed to get har top an bottom set, an the tuffey, orl out in one lump. We dint see them for the nex half hour. Oul Mrs.W— she kep a picken orf the tuffey, an earten on't, she dornt wearst nothen.

Granfar wus still a larfen, wen his pal Jimmur cum in (he knew we'd got suffen in the house). Jimmur's orlrite only he git on yar narves. He's one o' them tork-a-lot-do-a-little-men (theres plenty o' them about). He'd hed a few afore he cum to ours. Granfar say, learter on, 'Don't you hev tew much to drink Jimmur.' He say to Granfar, 'Yow ha' never seen me ha' more than I could carry.' Granfar say, 'No, praps not, but I ha' seen yow wen yow shud ha' meard two journeys.'

Learter on we orl hed a glars o' port an sum Xmas cearke (oul Mrs.W— hed two glarses) and she hulley prattled. As Granfar say, she ha' tew much to say, an ginerally say the wrong thing. Only the tother day, the Wicar gan har a lift in his little car, an wen he set har down she did say, 'Thank you werry much Wicar.' He say 'Dornt mention it,' she say 'Thas orlrite Wicar, I ount tell a soul.' Well, about harf arter ten Granfar dozed orf, so we closed the party. Jimmur sed as how he'd see Mrs.W— home (that just sewted har), but Granfar hed one eye open wen they went out o' the door. Well, orl the best. Fare yer well tergather.— Yars obediently,

THE BOY JOHN.


P.S.– Aunt Agatha, she say, 'Wen people send Xmas cards they shud rite on 'em with pencil. That wud searve sum money (nex year).'


## CHURCH GEART REGLARS

January 29th, 1952.

Deer Sar— Well, as Granfar say, 'There hearnt bin much to rite home about,' leartly. Things are a' gorne on werry steardy on tha farm, an so they are at ours. Grub fear to be a problem arter Xmas, an we hed a big party at ours a' tha' Boxen nite, yow couldn't sturrer, an Aunt Agatha used up orl har fats. She orfen say, 'I dornt know wot we're a gorne to hev for dinner today,' but then she allus fine suffen, an we enjoy it. Me an Granfar are werry fond o' sweard tarnips sliced an biled, then, wus the matter wi' fryen on 'em up the nexter day?

Granfar say there wus an oul chap uster wark along o' him fifty year ago, he hed a comical sayen, 'Weal, wine an winegar is werry good wiltles, I'll wow.' We ha' hed so much mutton leartly Granfar say he'll soon look like a sheep. Aunt Agatha say, 'Tha's better than looken like a pig, Granfar.'

Wen I wus a gorne home a Satiday mornen, I see a lot on 'em outside tha church geart, so I drawed up there. O' corse oul Mrs.W— an a few o' har reglars wi' there. There wus a wedden on, wot they'd only herd on the day afore. I herd there wus a young woman outer our willage a marryen a young feller outer the nexter willage. Well bor, yow wanted to ha herd them oul women, a' pullen that couple to pieces, just acoss they wore a bein' married at short nottes; bor they went true ther pedigree. An by the time they'd finished with 'em they hearnt got a character at all.

I dint stop for the wedden, but o' corse wen I got home I told Aunt Agatha wot I'd seen an herd. Aunt Agatha earnt a gossip, but she like to know wass a gorne on, specially if tha's a wedden. She say, 'Tha's a pity them women hearnt got northen better to do. I know orl about it. They're a respectable young couple, an they're a gitten married acos he's orf to Korea nex week.'

Wot dew yow think is har leartest? (Oul Mrs.W— I mean.) She recon har aunt died. Well that wornt har aunt really. That wus har mother's cousen by har fust husben. Well, Mrs.W— went to five plearces in this willage, wot Aunt Agatha know about, a borreren black hats an dresses for that funeral, pretty sure that were she'd borrered 'em, they wunt want 'em back. Aunt Agatha recon that she ha' borrered enough black to larst har for orl the funerals she'll ever go tew (includen har own). O' corse, she can wear different black dresses for different funerals, just to impress har 'church geart reglars'. The people wot she borrered 'em orf out recognise their 'left orfs' becos they are a better clars o' peeple than har, an dornt go to the searme sort o' funerals as wot she dew.

Well, fare yer well tergather.— Yars obediently,

THE BOY JOHN.

P.S.– Aunt Agatha, she say, 'Tha's better to hev a house too small at Crissmas, than too big orl the year.'

# MRS.W— PROPOSES

March 4th, 1952.

Deer Sar— Well, we ha' had another Shrof Tuesday, cum an' go, an' there wornt much diffus atween that day, an' any other Tuesday, 'cept we hed pancearks. As Granfar say, years ago, the schule children allus hed a harf day a tha Shrof Tuesday, an' so did the farm learborers, an' there wus a plowen metch for them, for a leg o' pork. But things are altered, as Granfar say, a lot on 'em hev a day a week orf nowadays, so they dornt hev time to hev harf a day orf a tha Shrof Tuesday. We dint hev no Walentines to year. Mrs.W—, she statted a torken to Aunt Agatha about Walentines Day. Aunt Agatha she say 'We carnt think about Walentines this year Mrs.W—, not in these sad times.'

Well the wather ha' been kind tew us leartly, we're a gittin on wi' wark on the farm, a gitten the land riddy for them oul sugar beet agin. Charlur, wot wark along a us, he went to a wedden in our willage an' he was a cummen home arterwards, he'd had a few you see, an' he was a bit unsteady on his pins, but he wus a mearken the best on it, on a frorsty an' slippery rud. Well just afore he met the Wicar (who wus a walken down to ours) he fell down, the Wicar helped him up and sed to him 'Charles, sinners walk in slippery places.' Charlur say 'So I see Wicar, but I'm blowed if I can.'

Granfar say Charlur dornt orfen teark tew much, only about once every Learp Year. Oh that remind me, oul Mrs.W— she a bin a sorter tryen to hang har hat up along a Granfar bein' as how this is Learp Year. He got a hull lot o' rigmarole wot cum by pust, there wus a sorter ryme wot sed:

> 'Oh, Granfar, Dar Granfar, I du luv yow so,
> Yow dornt fear to luv me –My heart's full o' woe.
> If yow married me a nice home we cud share,
> Now say "Yis" Granfar – You know tha's Learp Year.'
> From yar luven – You know hew. X X X X

Granfar, he wus suffen savidge, he hully mobbed. We new that cum from oul Mrs.W—, thow she'd disguised har ryten. Yow see she hearnt got no proper ryten pearpor; she allus borrer orf a Aunt Agatha. She dint notice, but she'd rit that ryme on the back of a bill from a shop in Norwich, that wus for suffen she hearnt paid for that sed on it: 'To Mrs.W—, one pair of stays, 5s 11d.'

Granfar say, did you sweep the fleas away from yar front dooor on the first o' March? He did.

Well fare yer well agin tergether.—Yars obediently,

THE BOY JOHN.


P.S.– Aunt Agatha, she say: 'The only difference Leap Year makes to housewives is there's one extra day's cooking – and washing up.'

# GRANFAR IS ONLY MODERATE

April 5th, 1952.

Deer Sar— Granfar, he ha' hed tha 'flu; well that worn't 'flu really, that wus a bad cold on his chist. Aunt Agatha, she see tew him, she wun't bother our busy Doctor. Oul Mrs.W—, she cum roun' wen she herd he wus moderate; she knew as how he allus got sum rum inter tha house wen he hed a cold (but she din't git none). She say to Granfar, 'I shu'd ha' tha Doctor; that dorn't corst northen now.' Granfar say, 'That I know I shorn't; there's tew many peeple a runnen' orf tew tha Doctor's now wi' northen hardly tha matter with 'em, an' yow are one on 'em. Yow got yar free spectickles, wot yow din't want, yar false teeth wot yow never use, an' I recon yow wish yow were bald-headed. Tha's peeple like yow wot are a ruinen' this here National Health skeme; every time yow hev tha belly eark, orf yow go to tha Doctor. Bor, if I wus yar doctor, I'd mix yow up a bottle o' fisic wot wu'd keep yow from runnen' far from yar house for a fortnight.'

She ceartenly is a rum woman. Aunt Agatha ask har to go to one of the Wendsday Evening Service. She say, 'No, thank yer, I only go to church wen there's suffen on.' Well, my Aunt Agatha she's as good as a nurse; she soon got Granfar better. She say to me, 'Yow know, John, wen anyone is ill, never arsk 'em wot they like, but meark 'em suffen light an' tearsty an' teark it up to 'em. I're ha' seen har tearken suffen nice to Granfar, on a tray wi' a nice white clorth on, an' that looked werry tempten'. O' corse, his main cure wus his own idea that wus plenty o' bilded onions, wi' a nice glars o' hot rum, wi' sum sugar an' butter in it larst thing at nite. He's better now.

His pal Jimmur cum to see him wen he wus better. They played a trick on oul Mrs.W—. Jirnmur, he rit a latter that statted 'Deer Sar' an' that wus addressed to Granfar, that sed as how his Uncle had died in London an' left Granfar £50, an' that wus signed by a London lawyer. Well, they put that in an envelope, sealed it, an' rit Granfar's nearme an' address, an' a tha April fule day mornen' Jimmur dropped that latter just inside oul' Mrs.W—'s front geart. Well, bor, she cum a spuffelen down to ours learter on. She say, 'Oh, Granfar, here's a latter I found tha's for yow, an' yow bin left £50.' He say, 'How'd yow know that?' She say, 'Wi, tha's orl over the willage.' He say, 'Yis, I lay yow a shillun' that is an orl.'

Well, he gan har the length o' his tongue, acos she swore she hearn't opened that latter. Granfar say, 'Well, if yow din't open it, how do yow know wot wus in it?' Wen she went we could see that she'd steamed that open. As Granfar say, 'She's an oul' wermin.' Fare yow well tergerther.— Yars obediently,

THE BOY JOHN.


P.S.– Aunt Agatha, she say, 'If people think you're a fule, keep your mouth shut, then they won't know.'

# THE PARISH COUNCIL

May 19th, 1952.

Deer Sar— I lay yow a shillun sum o' yow ha' bin a wunderen where I ha' bin a gitten tew leartly. Well, we ha' bin a slippen in tew it on the farm. We're well ahid, we ha' got orl the seeds in, orl 'cept a few row o' mangol, wot a' got to go in right down to yin ind o' tha' ten earkers where thay lay low. O' corse we ha' got our wark cut out ahid on us. The weeds git ahead o' tha seeds. That'll be hoe, hoe, hoe, for a week or tew now. There's one think about wark on a farm, by the time yow ha' got fed up wi' one jorb, there's a different jorb a cumen on.

Oh, we're in tha' fashen in our willage, we hed our parish council election larst week. O' corse, we du different here to wot yow du in Norridge. We dornt hev no pollytics in our willage, we wote for the man (or woman) wus a putten up. Yow see we know orl about orl on 'em wot are a putten up, tha's why sum on em git in (an also why sum on em dornt). As Aunt Agatha say, 'If yow want to know wot yar own willage peeple think on yer, well, put up for the parish council, you'll sune find out. That earnt how important yow think you are, thas just wot they think on yer.'

We hed ten on 'em put up for seven seats. Seven on 'em got in, an tree dint, an them tree wot dint git in wornt werry plearsed. Oul Mrs.W— she woted. She got harself titywearted up, as if she wus a gorne to sum posh funeral. She called in a cumen back. Granfar say, wot she know about woten dornt signify.

There was one woman put up that dint suit Mrs.W—. She say, 'I dornt hold wi women a bein on the parish council, so I crossed har out for a statt' (an blowed if that woman dint git in wi' one wote).

O' corse our butcher got on agin. He ha' bin on ten years, an he'll be on another ten if he look arter his customers like he ha' bin a duen on. Yow know wot I mean, an' we allus git sum twiddly bits too, for a week or tew afore tha election. The Wicar, he got on agin. Aunt Agatha say him bein' on top meark the council look respectable. Our Doctor tew, he's on. Harry, wot dint git on, sed parish council meetens gan him a 'pain o' the neck,' so praps the Doctor can cure that.

Granfar and Jimmur both woted then went an hed a harf-pint apiece (they allus du election time). Our marster he went in, he trearted 'em. The tork wus orl elections. Our marster told them a true tearle. He sed, larst winter, him and a friend, on a cold winter's night called up at a country pub. They ordered tew drinks, then see another rume were there was a fire, an sum peeple a torken. They drawed trew there, an they wore orl a argaren orl about a footparth. Well, our marster, wot new that part well, told 'em wot ort to be dun. Then a man at the hid o' tha tearble jumped up an sed, 'Excuse me Sar, but I dornt think yow ha' got anything to du with it at orl, your opinion dornt count, are yow aware this is our parish council meeten?' Well our marster he polygised, drank up, an wen they got outside they hed a good larf. Well, fare yer well tergerther.— Yars obediently,

THE BOY JOHN.

P.S.– Aunt Agatha, she say, 'If yow want to keep friends wi' the peeple in yer willage, well, keep orf the parish council.'


## MRS.W— LOOKS AFTER THE HENS

July 15th, 1952.

Deer Sar— Wot wi' tha heet an tha howen, tha ha' bin tew hot to rite leartly, but we ha' nearly done wi' the beet for a time. They werry near meet in the rows. A course we hetter be arter tha hay wen we shud ha' bin arter tha sugar beet, an arter the beet wen we shud ha' bin amon' tha hay. I can tell yow farmen is orl a job; still, everything look well on the farm ter year.

Our marster took us orl to tha Show. Granfar set in front. I arnt a gorne to tell yow northen about tha Show cos ya pearpers wor full on it fer tew or tree days, wi' sum luvely pictures tew. Me an Aunt Agatha went ter tha Flower Show and Granfar and his pal Jimmur hed a jam roun'. They fear ter ha' spent tha best part o' sum time a watchen tha hosses being shod. Granfar say, 'Jimmur bor, this smell more like oul time.' They wore a thinken about years ago, wen tha blacksmith's shop wus tha only plearce yow could go tew fer a yarn wen that wus wet.

Jimmur wornt well sum time back. Aunt Agatha say, 'Why dorn't yow gorne see the doctor, Jimmur?' He say, 'No, I'm my own doctor. I meark my own medicen. I ha' tew sorts, starter and stopper.

Oh, we hed to arsk oul Mrs.W— to look arter our hins wile we went to tha Show, cos Jimmur wunt be atumb to look arter 'em. The nite afore, Granfar gathered orl the guseberries an the nexter mornen he got up arly an gathered the strawberries (sum harf ripe). He wornt a gorn ter give that oul gal harf a chance to pinch anything. An tha larst thing afore we cum away he gathered up orl tha hins' eggs. Then wot dew yow think he did? He put tew oul hins' eggs, wot had bin setten on for weeks, inter a hin's nearst. (He litely marked 'em so as he shud know 'em.) Then instead o' hangen our house key up in the shud, he hung an oul key up wot wunt fit northern, an put the house key inter his porket. He say, 'John, dornt say northern ter yar Aunt Agatha about wot I ha' dun.'

65

Well, wen we got back home, oul Mrs.W— set there on a box outside ours wi' a fearce as long as a fiddle. She say, 'I dornt know wot you're a gorn to dew, yar key ount undew yar door.' Granfar say, 'Wot dew yow wanter git inter the house for?' She say, 'Ter see if things wor orlrite.' Granfar say, 'Things'll be orlrite as long as yow hearnt bin in.'

Granfar meard as if he got the key out o' tha shud, an arter we'd hed sum tea Aunt Agatha gan oul Mrs.W— four eggs for looken arter the hins, an she went home. Learter on, Granfar say, 'I'm in a bit o' a muddle now John. Them tew bad eggs ha' gone, I watched har a gorne up o' tha rud; I see har git them tew eggs out o' the fence. She ha' mixed them wi' them gooduns. I wish yar Aunt Agatha hearnt a gan har them four.' Well, fare yer well agin, tergether. Yars obediently,

THE BOY JOHN.

P.S.– Aunt Agatha, she say, 'That earnt wot gals know nowadays wot bother the parents. Tha's how they found out.'


## ANOTHER SET-TO WITH MRS.W—

September 6th, 1952.

Deer Sar— I recon as how yow never expected to hev a latter away from me a' tha' harvest time, did yer? Well, we ha' dun, an tha' stacks are thatched an orl. Granfar sed they uster du a harvest years ago in about nearly harf the time they teark now, thow they ha' got orl these new fearks nowadays. He sed they uster wark as long as they cud see, an rest wen that wus wet. He dornt like them there combines, he say they learve the peice looken werry untider, not like that uster look wen that wus mowed.

Now them oul sugar beet lay ahid on us. They're pretty good, thow sum on 'em look moderate. Our marster say thas acos they dint git the rain sune enuff.

Granfar an oul Mrs.W— ha' hed another set-tew. I shull heter explain fust, that sum time back Jimmur's cat hed kittens, an he gan Aunt Agatha one, then o' corse oul Mrs.W— (she's a proper oul copycat) she wanted one. Jimmur gan har one tew, only he meard har fetch hars. Well, larst Friday nite Mrs.W— cum down to ours acos we wore orl a gorne up to Yarmouth the nexter day on a special arter harvest bus. Well, that wus dark afore we got rid o' Mrs.W—. Aunt Agatha kep a given har hints about getten leart you see, Granfar wanted to warsh his feet afore he went out.

Well, arter she went, Aunt Agatha got the hot water an our big enamel bowl an we went to bed and left Granfar a dewen his feet. Wen he'd got one fut dun, and dried, that wus standen on a cork mat wot Aunt Agatha bought fer that parpus, an his other fut was in the warter, there cum a knock at the door. Granfar thort that wus someone for Aunt Agatha, acos she'll turn out to help anyone taken ill durin the nite. Well, he went a splatteren athort our rume, one dry fut an one wet, wi' his trousers an pants tarned up his knees; he opened the door an pearked out, an there stood oul Mrs.W— with a cat in har arms.

He say, 'Whatever dew yow want this time o' tha' nite?' She say, 'Yar cat follered me home. I put it down an hooshed it back ever so many times but that cum right home wi' me, so I ha' carried it orl the way back.' Granfar he looked back inter our rume, he say, 'That earnt our cat, our cat lay asleep there on the sofa. Wi wot yow ha' got there is yar cat, yow silly oul fule yow.'

Well, she werry near blarred. She say, 'Oh, I am dun up. Can I cum in an set down?' Granfar say, 'No, that yow carnt, not at this time o' tha nite. There's enough scandal in tha willage orl riddy,' he say. 'If yow want to rest, there's a plearse outside where yow can set as long as yow like, so good nite.' Well, thas orl fer now, so fare yer well tergerther.— Yars obediently,

THE BOY JOHN.

P.S.– Aunt Agatha she say: 'We are all sent here to help others.' Granfar say: 'Well, wot are the others sent for?'


## THE DAYS ARE GETTING SHORTER

November 3rd, 1952.

Deer Sar— We're a walken on 'em up, tha oul beet, I mean knocken an topen, knocken an topen. We're a gitten on 'em up farster 'en they can git away. Yer see, that ha' bin pritty good duin. My hart, if a putten tha clocks back hearnt a shoved us inter winter time in a hurry. That git leart sune o' a nite now, dornt it? Winter ter year fear to ha' statted at tha ind o' Augist, and Granfar say we're infer a long and sharp winter on account o' orl tha berries on the fences. Aunt Agatha say, 'We shull git trew it agin, orl bein alive an well.'

There earnt nothen exciten a gorn on in our willage. Our new Parish Council, they're a duin the best they ken under tha circumstances. Wen things go rite four 'em they teark tha' praise, wen they dornt go rite they say thas them wot are over 'em wus a holden on 'em up. We play cards at ours agin now. Oul Mrs.W— she cum sumtimes, but Granfar he ount play along o' har – he recon she cheart. She wus a tellen Granfar, tother nite, how har garden wanted duin, an as how she hed to git har coal and kindlin in. She say, 'Yer know, Granfar, If I could marry sum, not tew old, but respectable pensioner, we could git on

67

fearmus, an there'd be tew on us to share our troubles.' Granfar say, 'Well, farst o' orl no respectable pensioner wud marry yow an agin, wi' tew on yer, yow'd hev more than twice as many troubles to share.'

She cleared orf in a hurry arter that, but she cum down to ours the nexter nite. She wus upset, she wus orl o' a' muckwarsh. That feared as if she'd bin tryen to meark sum syrip out o' sum sugar beet (to searve har sugar). Granfar say, 'Where'd yow git yar beet from?' She say, 'Orf o' a big lump alongside o' tha rud.' He say, 'So yow stole em, did yer? Bor, yow'll git orl wus acumen tew ya!' Well, me an Aunt Agatha went down. That feared as if Mrs.W— hed cut tha beet up inter small squares, put 'em inter har big sorsepan over her irle stove. Well, arter an hour they biled over. She got flumexed an tried to pore sum into har other sorsepan (she ha' only got tew sorsepans). Well, by the time we got there, that wus a jorb. That syrip hed set hard, like tuffey; both sorsepans wore set hard, an har irle stove wus one sticker mass.

Aunt Agatha say, 'Well, yow hearnt searved much sugar to nite, Mrs.W—, an we carnt dew much to nite.' She say, 'John, go down to ours an bring back my irle stove an a sorsepan, an wen yow tell Granfar wa's happened, don't meark the wust on it.' Well, fare yer well tergerther.—Yars obediently,

THE BOY JOHN.

P.S.– Aunt Agatha hearn't got no postscrip this time, she's tew busy a gitten Mrs.W—'s irle stove to go agin.


## THE LONG WALK BACK ALONE

December 6th, 1952.

Deer Sar— I arnt a gorne to rite anything about them there oul sugar beet this time, acos I'm sick o' tha site on 'em. To think that them blumen, slussey, mudder oul beet are a learter on a gorne to be on yar tearble in the form o' nice white sugar – well, bor, tha's a mirracle how they dew it, earn't it?

Well, tha nites keep a-pullen in, don't tha? Granfar, he gan me a sly oul look; he say, 'Nice long nites for courten now John.' Well I gan that gearme up afore I properly statted. Yer see, wen my young woman statted a-chewen gum, an' a-callen me 'Buddy' (more like a Norridge gal), well, I chucked har up, an' besides, she lived a mile away from ours, rite down to yin ind o' our willage. I dint mind a seein on 'er home, that wus the long walk back, alone, wot chucked me orf a-courten.

Oh! Oul Mrs.W—, she ha' hed a corn wot ha' been tormenten har, that wus on har toe, that wus a sorft one, so she couldn't cut it. She told Aunt Agatha about it (but she wunt show it tew 'er). Well, wen Aunt Agatha went up ter Norridge, she bort sum corn plarsters; they wore like rings, they fear to stick on round the corn, an' that stop yar corn from harten yar shew. Mrs.W— say, 'Wot dew it say on tha box?' Aunt Agatha red tha directions: 'Carefully clean the affected.' Mrs.W— say, 'That dornt mean I're got to warsh me hull fut, do it? If I just warsh me toe wi' tha corn on that shud do, shun't it?' Granfar he heard har, he gan a funny oul grunt. Then she wanted to borrer an easy-fitten oul shew orf o' Aunt Agatha. Well, then Granfar hed a mow in, he say, 'I shud think yow ha'got enuff bewts an' shews in yar house – wot yow ha' bort at rummidge searles – to wear comfitable if yar gut hed got eather corns or bunions, or both.' She slid orf after that.

Oh! Ha' yow meard yar Xmas pudden? We're meard ours. Aunt Agatha allus meark hars the week afore 'Stur-up Sunday.' Tha's a jorb agin ter year, a-gitten the stuff for it, earn't it? Now if any on yer could let my Aunt Agatha ha' sum rearsons (we dornt want 'em for northen) we could dew ya sum eggs. Granfar, he did sturrer the pudden ter year. If yow can remember, he hed a cold in his hid larst year, an' Aunt Agatha sed that won't ha' bin hygeenic, an' yit searf, for him to ha' hed his hid over that pudden bearsen then. We shull be orl rite fer our Xmas dinner, our marster is given' on us a fat cockrell, so fare yer well til Xmas, an' that ount be long now.— Yars obediently,

THE BOY JOHN.


## GRANFAR READY FOR ANYTHING

December 24th, 1952.

Deer Sar— Well, here's Xmas on top on us afore we know where wi' are. Acordenly to the weather we ha' bin a heven on leartly, we ha' hed our winter orl ridy, hearnt wi'? Me, an Granfar tew, are fed up wi', as he say 'a pruggen about these here dark mornens.'

Now regarden them there oul sugar beet, we hearn't got 'em orl way, but we hev gor' 'em orl up. I're seen so much o' them oul beet leartly, that they ha' put me clean orf a eaten a parsnips (an' I like parsnips).

Well we fear orl set for Xmas, our marster gan Granfar his usual bottle o' rum. Granfar say tha's good for a cold, but I nutice that by the time Granfar git his cold, that bottle is ginerally empty.

Me an' Granfar ha bort Aunt Agatha a pair o' slippers for our Xmas present, they are orl lined wi' fur. We hed a jorb acos we din't know wot size. I sed to Granfar 'Shull we arsk Mrs.W—? She might know.' Granfar say, 'What *har*!?'

However a leardy friend o' Aunt Agatha's knew the size, an' got a pair wen she went up to Norridge, orl unbeknown to Aunt Agatha, o' corse.

Granfar he bort a bottle o' port wine, for tha house. Oh, oul Mrs.W— she sent Granfar a Xmas present ever so long ago, that was a jar o' pickled onions. Fancy a senden Granfar pickled onions, an' him wi' only one tooth, an' thas in front. (He gan em to Jimmur.)

Aunt Agatha told us Mrs.W— wuss a heven har Xmas dinner along wi' us. Well, then Granfar statted a putten on his parts. He say, 'If she's a cummen here, yow can teark that plant orf a that roun tearble agin the winder an' let har set there on har own, wi' four on us a setten round our tearble I ha' got to set eyther alongside on 'er, or else rite opposit ha', an that'd put me clean orf a my Xmas dinner.'

Aunt Agatha say, 'Now Granfar, dorn't teark on like that, I're arsked Jimmur ter cum to dinner, so I'll meark Mrs.W— set tha other side of him.'

I recon as how yow orl wondered why there worn't no pustscript to my larst latter. Aunt Agatha did send one, an' o' corse we orl nuttised that worn't there. Granfar say to Aunt Agatha, 'You din't put in suffen wot yow shunt a dun, did yer?' She just looked at him an' sed, 'Granfar.'

Aunt Agatha found out that wus a misteark by sum one in tha' orfice wot din't tork Norfick, they sed they wore sorry an' Aunt Agatha she's forgiven 'em.

Oh, our pudden is a good un, Aunt Agatha she meard a tearster, we hed it larst Sunday, that wus luvely.

Well, once agin, we an' Aunt Agatha an' Granfar, we orl wish yow an' yar staff (an' tha' young man who left out the pustscript) a Werry Happy Xmas. Them there wishes go tew orl yow wot read this.

So, fare yow well tergether.—Yars obediently,

THE BOY JOHN.

P.S.– Aunt Agatha, she say, 'Give a present an' forget it. Receive one – an' never forget.'


## A NEW YEAR'S PARTY

January 10th, 1953.

Deer Sar— Well, here's Christmas cum an' gon afore we know where wi' are. We got messed up for our Christmas party. Jimmur he worn't earble to cum, acos he hed to go an see his sister wot wuss sadly, an oul Mrs.W— she didn't cum acos she hed a bad cold, consequently, me and Granfar ha' been a liven on sossige rolls and mince pies since Christmas. A Christmas Day Aunt Agatha took Mrs.W— har Christmas dinner, an blowed if Granfar dint open his hart, and send har sum rum. He pored sum rum outer his bottle inter a little bottle, then filled it up wi' warter (so there'd look a nice lot).

Well we hed a New Year's party insted. We hed wot Aunt Agatha called a high tea. Jimmur he set nexter Granfar, wi' Mrs.W— the yin side o' Jimmur. Arter tea we played cards. Granfar dint play, he reconed as how he'd got roomatism in his hans. (He ount play wi' Mrs.W—, he recon she cheart.) Learter on Aunt Agatha left us fer a time to go an see a woman wot wornt well, she dint go empty handed neyther, an she pored us orl out a glass o' port wine afore she went.

Mrs.W— she was full o' prattle. Do yow know what? When Jimmur an Granfar went an hed a harf pint a tha' noontime, they see oul Mrs.W— nip round to tha back o' tha Crown. Jimmur say, 'I recon tha' oul gal is a gorne to prime harself up fer tha party to nite.' Granfar he got inter a muddle, he hid his bottle o' rum up, wen he new Mrs.W— was a-cummin, then he forgot where he'd hid it. We wore a hunten for it, high an' low.

Oul Mrs.W—, she cum trew outer our back plearce, she say, 'Wot ever are yow a dewen on?' Granfar say, 'We're a playen a gearm.' She say, 'Can I cum in?' Granfar say, 'No, that yow carnt, this is fer men only.' Jimmur found it at last, that wus in the shew cubboard, shoved inter one o' Granfar's high-low shews. Well we set there a torken, then every now an agin wen Mrs.W— wornt a looken, Jimmur kep a putten sum rum inter har glass, arter a time she say, 'I think I'll git inter tha' easy chair I fear tired.'

She was sune asleep. Granfar say, 'Put that there antermacasser over har fearce, dornt she'll gi' me nitemare. We'll hev a gearme o' nap' (his hans wore orlrite for nap). Wen Aunt Agatha cum back she say, 'Is she orlrite?' Granfar say, 'I think she tarned a little faint.' Aunt Agatha wen she uncovered 'er she say, 'Faint! by tha' look o' har fearce she'll sune fly afire.' Aunt Agatha hed an idea wot wus up.

We hed sum supper an strong corfee an wot amused Granfar most wus wen Jimmur took Mrs.W— home, fare yer well tergether.— Yours obediently,

THE BOY JOHN.

P.S.– Aunt Agatha, she say, 'How nice that is to do northen, an then rest afterwards.'

71

# GRANFAR AND A GIFT OF CLOTHES

March 10th, 1953.

Deer Sar— Thas a good jorb the werther ha' hild fine leartly, earnt it? We ha' got on a rumen on tha farm. We're got our oots in, an tha weart look well, an we're a gitten the land fit fer that there other croorp, yow know wot I mean (only I dornt want to mention sugar beet – not yit). Aunt Agatha she sed I dint orter rite one o' my latters wen so many peeple wore a sufferen from them terrible floods. So thas why I hearnt rit leartly. In our willage we nearly orl lent a hand one way o' another. Several o' our chaps went down to Pallen a fillen a san bags, an our Wicar he was one on 'em .

Aunt Agatha, she collected a lot o' clothes for the W.V.S. an Granfar he wheeled 'em down ter tha schulerume. Old Mrs.W— she brort a bundle o' clothes an shews. Arter she'd gon, an Aunt Agatha hed gon trew 'em, she say, 'Granfar! teark the hull lot on 'em inter tha garden an bann 'em, thas orl they're fit for.' Granfar he went orf wi' that bundle inter tha garden an he was a' hully a mutteren.

Arter a time he cum back his fearce wus red an he wus suffen savidge, Aunt Agatha say, 'Well ha' yow bant 'em?' He say, 'Yis I hev, an I wish that oul gal hed a bin here, I'd a shuved har on torp, she's a proper datty oul waarmen. If I'd a known I'd a carried them out on a pitchfork. I ha cort one o' har fleas a carryen that bundle under my arm. Now I shull heter go upstairs an strip. I wunt mind so much if that wornt one o' har fleas.'

Granfar wus upstairs, best part o' sum time, Aunt Agatha shouted up to him, she say, 'Ha' yer cort it?' He say, 'Not yit; arsk John to bring up my spectickles.' Well I took 'em up, he say, 'Yow dornt wanter cum in, I'm in a bit o' a muddle, shove' em unind the door.' Well arter a time he cum down, he sed he thort he'd cort it. He was dressed up in his Sunday suit, acos he an Jimmur wore a gorne to tha oul earge pensions' tea, wot we allus hev on a Shroof Tuesday.

They hed a luvely time. Granfar won sum coushies, they wore peppermints. He an Jimmur set there a sucken on most o' tha nite. Granfar gan Aunt Agatha sum, but he dint give oul Mrs.W— none, an he upset har lerter on. Ya see she was a showen harself orf, bigoty like, hullen har legs about, pretenden to darnce. Arterwards she cum up to Granfar an say, 'Wot do yow think o' that for an old 'en, Granfar?' He say, 'Well, afore yow meark an exhibition o' yarself in public agin, yow want to stop at home an hev a day's warshen.' Well bor, I thort she wus a gorn to hit 'im.

Well fare yer well agin tergerther.—Yars obediently,

THE BOY JOHN.


P.S.-Aunt Agatha, she say, 'You carnt keep trouble from cumen, but dornt give it a chair to set on.'

# A SETBACK AFTER TOMBLAND FAIR

May 1st, 1953.

Deer Sar— They're a cumen up a rumen arter tha rain; yow ken werry nye see 'em uper tha ryndges, an' now they're got sum moysture, orl they want is sum warm nites, then we ken find harf Norridge a job a hoen on 'em, only you'll heter bring yar own hoe .

Gal Meary, o' Ingham, yow rit to know why I hearnt rit leartly. Well I ha' bin moderate since Tombland Fair (but I'm orlrite now). Me an' another boy biked home from the Fair a rare oul strook, that hully meard us sweat; well then we stood an mardeled best part o' sum time – an' that's how I cort my cold. I hed to heve tha Doctor, an he an' Aunt Agatha sune got me on tha mend agin.

Granfar wus werry good wen I wus laid up; he useter do orl the jorbs I useter do for Aunt Agatha, an' wen I wus a gitten batter Aunt Agatha meard me lots o' nice things, like blewmonges an' jellies, an' I allus left sum fer Granfar.

Oul Mrs.W— dint come down while I wus laid up, acos she sed she might catch my complaint. O' corse, I'd only got a bad cold. I wus batter wen she did cum, an' me an' Granfar wore a heven a bit o' fulery an' a larfen. (O' corse she's a miserable oul woman, an' look it.) She say to Aunt Agatha, 'That boy John is allus merry an' bright an' a larfen he ha' so much on't.' Aunt Agatha (she allus stan' up fer me) she say, 'Look here, Mrs.W— wen yow git home open yar Bible (if yow can find it) an' turn to the 17th Chapter of Proverbs an' read the 22nd verse, an' you'll find the boy John earnt far out.'

Oh, since then, oul Mrs.W— an' Granfar ha hed a set-tew. Our marster told Granfar as how he could cut his self sum pea sticks outer tha heater plantan. Well, he loaded foar grate bunches unter his wheel barrer, he couldn't see ahid on 'im on account o' tha sticks, but he kep' tha proper side of tha rud an' kep' his eye on the brow o' tha holl.

Orl o' a sudden he fear to hit suffen, an' he heard a woman yell out. He went ahid o' his barrer, an' there wus oul Mrs.W— a scrabben harself up orf the rud. Well, bor, they hully mobbed each other. Granfar sed, 'Wi surely yow cud see me a cumen?' She say, 'Yis, I see a barrer load o' sticks a cumen, only wen yow hit me I wus tarned roun', a looken at that woman wot just passed me.'

Me an Aunt Agatha larfed wen Granfar told us. Aunt Agatha say, 'Well, surely yow apologised to har, Granfar.' He say, 'Polygise! Wot me? Wot to har? If I'd ha known that wus har I'd ha' crowded the barrer over top on 'er an' that won't a bin my fault if she'd a got jamped on.'

Well, tha's orl fer now, so fare yer well tergathar.—Yars obediently,

THE BOY JOHN.

P.S.– Aunt Agatha she say, 'You can always tell a Norfolk man – but you can't tell him much.'

# GRANFAR WAS AT ST. BENET'S

August 15th, 1953.

Deer Sar— Thas a jorb to git a latter rit this time o' tha year. Just arter I'd rit my larst latter a young woman wot know me she say, 'Yow hearnt hed a latter in leartly, John.' I say, 'Wi, there wus one in a tha Monday, that show yow dornt read yar pearper properly.' We orl enjoy them luvely pictures yow hev in yar pearper. We allus hev time to look at them; Granfar still corl 'em gays.

We orl went to tha Sarvice at St. Benet's Abbey; we go every year. Our marster took us in his motor. That wus luvely to hev the Queen Mother an' Princess Margaret there, a joinen in tha Sarvice wi' orl us Norfick peeple an' the wisitors as homely as cud be. Our Bishop wus as nice as ever; he meard everyone fear easy as soon as ever he stated his address; he say, 'My first tew wads to yow are "Sit down".'

Granfar, he set down, but he wus set fast wen that cum to git up agin. Tew young leardies orf a yot, wi' short shorts on, lent him a hand, an' they meard a rare fuss o' him. He wus suffen plearsed acos oul Mrs.W— wus a watchen a him. She cum on a bus, only she would hang round Aunt Agatha. She wus dressed orl in black, in a long skart an' a black hat wi' a feather. That meard yar hot to look at 'er.

If yow remember, larst year there wus a quire boy walked in a deek; thas a deep deek, covered wi' green weeds so that look just like the meysh. Well, a young leardy walked in this year, an' oul Mrs.W— wud a bin in ter year if Aunt Agatha hearnt a hallered out tew 'er. Granfar say, 'Yow orter ler 'er a went.'

Oul Mrs.W— meard Granfar suffen savage larst Satiday. She hed sum releartions a gorne away, an' she arsked Granfar if he'd crowd their luggage down ter tha' steartion. He say, 'Tearnt ser likely; yow can borrer tha barrer if yow like.'

Well, Jimmur cum down a tha nite time, he say, 'Yow hed a rare session down to tha Crown as noontime, dint yer, Granfar?'

'Crown!' sed Granfar, 'I hearnt bin outer tha garden geart terday.' Jimmur say, 'Thas a rummen, I thort yow were there, acos yar barrer stood outside tha Crown nearly orl noontime.' Wot Granfar sed then I dussent rite. Fare yow well agin.— Yars obediently,

THE BOY JOHN.

P.S.– Aunt Agatha, she say, 'To enjoy happiness you must share it wi' someone.'

# MRS. W— DOES THE POOLS

October 15th, 1953.

Deer Sar— We're in amun 'em agin an my hart hearnt we got sum oul clinkers ter year.

I'll tell yow wot, them grate oul beet teark sum pullen up, then yow ha' got to knock 'em an hull 'em in ringes, an then hull 'em up on ter tha tumble. My hart, we hed tha back eark fer a statt, but we hed a spell a fine weather to help us, thow thas a rainen now (tha's why I'm a riten).

We got trew harvest orlrite, thow we got hild up wi' spells or wet weather. Granfar say wi' orl these new fearks they dornt git trew harvest as quick as they use tew. He say, 'We useter wark orl hours o' tha fine weather an hev a "setten in" if that wus wet.' He dornt believe in these here comberneartions wot cut the corn an trosh at tha searm time. He say no man, yit no machine, can dew tew or tree jorbs at the searme time an dew 'em orl well.

Oh, oul Mrs.W—, she cum to ours tha' tother nite, she'd bin a giten them there football coupons trew tha pust (I recon saveral on ya' get 'em). She brort 'em down to ours an there wus only Granfar at home (Aunt Agatha hed gone out to teark sum hot brorth to a woman wot wornt well). Mrs.W— asked Granfar if he knew anything about how she shud fill up har coupons acos she'd red where saveral peeple hed won 75,000 pouns. He pretended he knew (acos he din't).

Well, she layed her coupons on tha' tearble, he put on his spectickles an he say ter har, 'Yow ha got to fill up these here squares wi' nortes an crorses, onler yow mustn't git em so as yow git tree nortes an tree crorses all in a line.' Well, she went orf home ter dew har coupons.

O' corse, Granfar dornt know northern about coupons, yit football, thow he allus say to me 'How'd Norridge git on a' Satiday John?' Wen I got home he told me about Mrs.W— an har coupons, an wot he'd done, an he say ter me 'Dornt you tell yar Aunt Agatha about tha' coupons John, dew she'll mob me.'

I dornt believe I ever told yow about Closh, he's a jorb. He cum to ours the tother nite to see Granfar. Well bor, he'd tork tha hind leg orf a dicker; he know everything wus a' gorne on in our willage, an everything wus a cumen on tew. We call him 'The Eastern Daily Press' acos he hev orl the news (of the willage I mean). I lay yow a shillen, yow wot live in willages ha' got a chap like Closh in yar willage, hearn't yer? Well, tha rain's a earsen up, an so 'em I. So fare yer well tergether.— Yars obediently,

THE BOY JOHN.

P.S.– Aunt Agatha, she say, 'It's a pity we carn't live in the past – it would be so much cheaper.'

# JIMMUR'S RABBIT

November 23rd, 1953.

Deer Sar— We're a gitten them oul sugar beet orf tha' land farster than wot tha factory ken teark 'em in; thas acos we're hed a nice lot o' open whether, thas why when yow Norridge peeple when yow go about (if yow go about) see grate oul lumps o' beet a layen alongside o' tha rud.

I see as how you ha' hed sum latters in yar pearper about my latters. Well I do tha' best I can, wi wot I're got to do it with, an I cant dew more 'an that, can 'er?

That leardy wot rit an sed as how I wanted more wowels to meark use on is about rite. Anyhow I fear as if I want suffen wot I hearnt got, so as you can read it tha' searme as I mean yer tew.

Granfar he git his spectarkils on an git trew most o' yar pearper bi' nitefall. He red that leardy's latter, only he trort 'wowels' wor part of yer inside.

Mrs.W—, she dun sum waashen for Closh so he gan har a rabbit (he's a rare poacher). Well Jimmur, he'd bin a duin Mrs.W—'s garden an she ask him if he'd skin this rabbit, which he did. Well then, Jimmur statted tellen har about a disease wot rabbits hed nowadays.

Well that chooked har orf o' that rabbit so Jimmur sed he'd tearke it home an try it on his ferrets. Now tew nites learter Jimmur brought Granfar a piece o' rabbit pie. Granfar enjoyed it, he dint know the particulars then (Granfars still orlrite). Aunt Agatha was werry annoyed wi' Jimmur, she hully mobbed him, he stood there a wibbelen his cap up, acos he wus narvous, she told him he orter be ashearmed o' hisself a robben Mrs.W— o' har rabbit.

Mrs.W— cum down to ours tother nite ter boorer a big sorsepan (Aunt Agatha orfen larf an say, 'Mrs.W— boorer so much orf o' me, that I feel more at home in har house than I do my own').

I noticed wen Mrs.W— went away, Aunt Agatha put harf a pork cheese an a grate piece of apple tart inter har sorespan, thats to help mearke up fer tha' rabbit she never hed.

Well fare yer well tergether till Christmas, an that ount be long now.— Yars obediently,

THE BOY JOHN.


P.S.– Aunt Agatha, she say: 'A woman is judged by her company – but not until after she's left.'

# THE GOOSE GOES UNCOOKED

December 24th, 1953.

Deer Sar— As Granfar sed a short while ago, 'We shull hev Xmas on top on us afore wi' know where wi' are,' and so it tis, earnt it? An I'm a' gorn to forgit orl about them there oul sugar beet fer a day or tew, so I shornt mention 'em.

Our marster ha' gan Aunt Agatha a bottle o' port wine, an Granfar a bottle o' rum fer Xmas, so he's set up orlrite. Tha's funny how, ginerally every Friday nite arter Xmas, Granfar allus hev a tissic on his chist – till that rum is orl gone.

We ha' hed a goose since the summer wot we ha' bin a rearen for our Xmas dinner. We orl got fond on it; that'd foller Aunt Agatha down a tha' garden wen she hung out her warshen, an allus be along o' Granfar in the garden, an that wud feed outer his hand, but that'd go fer oul Mrs.W— (an that plearsed Granfar a rumen).

Well wen the time cum for Granfar to teark that goose away to be killed, an plucked, he stood a looken down at that goose fer best part o' sum time. That looked up at him, an he sed that hed tears in its eyes (an so hed Granfar). He say to me 'John bor, I can't dew it, if that goose wus killed an cooked, I coont eart it; that'd be like earten one o' tha' family.'

Well, he went indoors an sed tew Aunt Agatha, 'Wunt that be better if we hed a couple o'chickens fer our Xmas dinner ter year? I'll pay fer one on 'em.' I cud see my Aunt Agatha wus releaved, acos she's as murehearted as Granfar. She sed 'Yis' at once.

Well, wen Granfar went orf ter order them chickens, Aunt Agatha went out an meard a rare fuss o' that goose, an she shed a few tears tew. When Granfar cum back he say, 'Tha's warth while a keepen that goose, John; if thas only ter put tha wind uper oul Mrs.W— wen she cum here, a poken har nose in where that earnt wanted. An' another thing, ever since we ha' bin torken about heven that goose fer Xmas, she ha' been a sayen how fond she is o' goose drippen on tust. She'll ha' to spreard suffen else on har tust now, John.'

Oh, Granfar he put on his parts wen Aunt Agatha sed Mrs.W— wus a heven her Xmas dinner along o' us. Aunt Agatha say, 'For goodness seark be more sooshibul, Granfar; git more o' tha' Xmas spirit intew yer.'

Granfar say, 'I shull want a different sort o' spirit inter me, to fearce up to that oul gal a setten at our tearble.' Aunt Agatha say, 'Well, you know Jimmur is a' cumen, and he ken set along-side yow.'

Well, once agin I wish you, an yar starf an orl wot read yar pearper a werry Happy Xmas, an that signify fer Aunt Agatha an Granfar an orl, so fare-yer-well tergerther.— Yars obediently,

THE BOY JOHN.

P.S.– Aunt Agatha, she say, 'Dorn't stand too much on your dignity – it can be very slippery.'

# CHRISTMAS DAY'S HARMONY

January 2nd, 1954.

Deer Sar— Farst o'orl, I're gotter say thank yer ter orl on yer wot sent me latters and Christmas cards. One leardy wot live in Norridge rit as how she send orl my latters to har neece, wot live in Alaska. Thas a rumen, earnt it? I thort that 'ed a bin tew cold to dew any readen up there.

Thank yow too, Sar, fer yar Christmas card, a country seen, wi' snow on it. Granfar say thas tha best plearse fer snow, on a Christmas card. Aunt Agatha ha stood yar card on the middle o har chimley peece, atwicks har tew chiner dorgs.

Well, we ha hed a luvely Christmas. Me an Aunt Agatha went to church to tha arly service. Granfar got up tew, an wen we cum back he'd got tha coal an warter an kindlen in, a good fire a-gorne, wi tha kittle a bilen, he'd swep up, tew (in plearces). We hed our brakfuss, fried sossages, an foar tomarters, wot he gathered out o' his garden a Christmas mornen – wotter yer think o' that. Arter brakfuss we undid our presents. There wuss tew pair o' socks an a wrapper fer Granfar, a pair o' warm slipshews fer me, an me an Granfar gan Aunt Agatha a tea kosy an a hot warter bottle.

Mrs.W— gan Aunt Agatha a varse, fer flowers, an dew yow know wot? That wuss the werry searme varse wot Aunt Agatha won at a whist drive five year ago. Aunt Agatha gan it tew oul Mrs.W— tree year ago fer Christmas. I remember Mrs.W— a' sayen at tha time, 'Thank yer werry much, I shan't part wi' that time I'm alive.' O' corse, Aunt Agatha she thanked har for tha varse, but never sed nurthen. Granfar wuss a-gorn tew, only he cort my Aunt Agatha's eye, so he just garped, but never spook.

Jimmur an Granfar went down ter tha Crown fer a couple afore dinner, they'd both hed a trim up er tha day afore, so they looked kinder tidy (they wornt leart back). Mrs.W— she cum in cold, so Aunt Agatha gan har a glars o' port wine, that soon put har rite.

We had a real good dinner, only we dint ha no parsneps ter year. Granfar dug sum up weeks ago ter git tha frost, as he say they hearnt got no tearst in em if they hearnt hed a frost on em.

We hed a glars o' port wine wi our dinner, then a cup o' tea arter dinner (oul Mrs.W— hed tew) then we orl rested. Mrs.W— she went to sleep, an dint she snore. Jimmur say, 'I can cure har a snoren.' Granfar say, 'How?' Jimmur say, 'Wi, wearke har up.' Granfar say, 'No fare, Jimmur bor, let yow har snore.' Well that wornt long after that Granfar an Jimmur dozed orf, so then me an Aunt Agatha went an warshed up an finished in time to weark em orl up to hear our Queen's speech.

Well I hearnt got time to tel wot happened learter on; we dint want much tea. Arter that we set an torked an Granfar got his rum bottle out. That statted to

rain wen that was time to go, an dint that plearse Granfar to see ould Mrs.W—
a-hangen unter har amberaller, an Jimmur a-hangen unter oul Mrs.W—, a
gorne downer our garden path.

Well, once agin, fare yer well tergether.— Yars obediently,

THE BOY JOHN.

P.S.– Aunt Agatha she say, 'If a woman wants to spend a few minutes on her
own, she only wants to start washing-up.'

## AN OLD-FASHIONED WINTER

February 16th, 1954.

Deer Sar— That ha' bin a jorb orl that frosty wether fer our marster to find us
a jorb on tha farm, acoss he dorn't like tha idea o' standen on us orf. We ha'
clearned orl tha holls out, cut down sum grate oul fences an wen we finished a
muck carten, he say, 'I dornt know wot I'm a gorn to find yow chaps ter dew
now John, unless yow cart orl that muck back inter tha yard agin.

Howsumever, we ha cut up enuf firewood to larst till next Christmas, an
we're now busy a white-warshen tha barn (inside).

I got unter Granfar's track, about this weather. I say ter him, 'That only
larst month wen yow sed as how we dornt git them oul fashened winters like
we used tew.' I say, 'Yow wore wrong Granfar.' He say, 'Yis, an so wore yow
wen yow sed as how the Arsenal wud beart Norridge City.'

Oh, we wore orl suffen excited wen we see our foetoes in yar pearper,
wot wore supposed to be us, in that pantomime wot them leardies got up at
Horefton. Me an Aunt Agatha went an see it, that wuss luvely. O' corse we
din't let them know who we wore. Granfar larfed wen he see his foetoe in yar
pearper. He say, 'I dornt look as smart as that dew I John?'

Oul Mrs.W— was ever so plearsed, acos she earnt harf as good looken
as har likeness in tha pearper wuss, an Aunt Agatha hed a nice kind fearce,
just like my proper Aunt Agatha. Acos that Boy John in tha play is a lot batter
looken than wot I am. Granfar say 'His nose earnt so big as yars John.'

Mrs.W— she cum to ours, acos har pump was fruss up. Granfar wunt
go down, besides that wornt fit fer him ter go out, so we sent ward down ter
Jimmur. Well while she wuss here that cum on a snowen a rumen, so Aunt
Agatha lent har har rubber butes ter go home in.

Mrs.W— cum down to ours, nexter mornen. She wuss in a rear stearte.
She sed sh'ed lorst one o' Aunt Agatha's rubber butes. Aunt Agatha say, 'How
cum yow ter dew that?' She say, 'I dornt know, orl I know is that wornt on wen

I got home.' Well, I went an hed a hunt 'er tha nune-time fer that bute, atween ours an hars. I coont find it, then I see Jimmur. He say 'Wotter yow a looken for John?' I told him. He say, 'Wi, the lanleardy at tha Crown found a rubber bute a standed up in tha snow, juss outside har back entrance, this mornen. I lay yow a shillen thas tha one.' That wuss an orl.

Wen I went back an told them at home wot hed happened, Granfar he let fly. He say, 'An she told us she went straight home,' an he sed a lot more, 'till Aunt Agatha hed to corl him ter order.

Well, fare yer well tergerther.— Yars obediently.

THE BOY JOHN.

P.S.– Aunt Agatha, she say, 'Trust no memory however bright. Put it down in black and white.'

## THE BOY JOHN'S PANCAKE DAY

March 9th, 1954.

Dear Sar— Well, March cum in ruff, dint it? Granfar say: 'March hek ham, cum in like a lion, go out like a lam,' an' he say we shornt git no sattled weather 'till arter tha wearn o' tha mune. (We shull see, shurnt wi?)

Granfar was up arly o' tha farst o' March, searme as he ha' allus dun far years, ter sweep tha fleas away from tha front door, but he found snow te year. He say, 'Here wi go John, snow an' fleas orl mixed up tergether, we shornt git troubled wi' them fer a time.' Then he got busy an' swep' tha snow away right up t' tha garden geart, tha coal shud door an' another door.

Oh, we hed sum excitement in our willage a' tha Shruf Tewsday. Aunt Agatha wus a gitten' har stuff ridy t' meark har pancearkes, yow know, a hull lot a' like yaller pearst in a bowl, wen a boy on a bike cum down an' sed Mrs.W—'s house wus afire. Aunt Agatha left everything an' hurried orf down there; Granfar he follered on at a jog trot.

Wen they got down there, they found that wornt har house; that wus har chimley wot wus afire. Jimmur wus there, he'd sorter took charge. Aunt Agatha say, 'Was tha best thing t' dew, Jimmur?' Jimmur say, 'Dornt dew northen, let har barn out, she ount teark no harm, thas how we uster sweep 'em years ago. I know thas a thatched roaf, but thas covered wi' snow; besides, I ha' got a ladder up agin tha earves, just in cearse.' Well, as Jimmur sed, she barnt harself out.

Aunt Agatha say, 'How cum that t' fly afire?' Mrs.W— say, 'Well, tha fire wus werry low, I wanted it t' git up to dew my pancearkes, so I put sum paraffen irle on it, an I wus a blowen' on it wen that flapped.' Well, har eyebrows wi' barnt an' har fearce wus black; lor she looked a jorb.

Howsomever, they lent a hand t' clear up, Granfar an' orl. He'll help anybody wen they're in a muddle (even har). Har batter (I coon't think o' that waad afore) wus covered wi' soot. Aunt Agatha say, 'Dornt yow worry Mrs.W—, arter we ha' cleared up a bit, cum yow down to ours an' hev yow yar pancearkes along or us.'

Arter they'd dun wot they could, Jimmur and Granfar left, Jimmur allus hev pancearkes at ours on a Shruf Tewsday, an' they allus hev a wet down to tha Crown afore dinner. They set in the tap rume, then arter a time they see Mrs.W— slip roun ter tha back. Jimmur say, 'Tha poor oul gal is a gorne to hev suffen t' git har narves back.'

Well, she cum to ours sum time arter Granfar an' Jimmur. Aunt Agatha sed 'My waad, Mrs.W—, that fire ha' give yow a rare red fearce.' Jimmur he winked at Granfar, an' Granfar gan him a sly oul look, but they never sed northern, they knew that wornt tha fire alone wot gan har that colour. Well, fare yer well tergerther.— Yars obediently,

THE BOY JOHN.

P.S.– Aunt Agatha, she say, 'The more yow say, the less people remember.'


## AUNT AGATHA AT THE DOCTOR'S

June 22nd, 1954.

Deer Sar— That fear to be sum long time since I larst ritt ter yow, but dew you know wot, farst o' orl I wus moderate fer best part o' sum time, then them oul sugar beet cum along, an that ha' bin, how, how, how, wi' yer back a earken like billyo, fer tha' furst week. Them beet dornt grow like they ort tew (thow the weeds do); we want sum warm whather to git them a gorn, wi' sum sun ter put sum sugar in tew em.

Then agin, there hearn't bin nurthan happen in our willage leartly. As tha' boy say, 'Nurthan to rite home about.'

My Aunt Agatha, as yow know, ha' got a rare sense o' humur. Well she went down to tha Doctor's to fetch a bottle o' medisen for a woman wot wornt well. She sed there wus two women who met in tha' waiten rume, yow know, a couple o' his 'reglars'. You know tha sort I mean if yow live in a country willage. One on em sed ter tha other, 'I hearnt seen yer down here leartly, hearnt yer bin well?'

Doctor wus a torken ter my Aunt Agatha, outside, yow see he confide in her, wen up cum oul Mrs.W— (another 'reglar'). Doctor sed, 'Morning, Mrs.W—, how are you?' She say, 'quite well, thank yer, Doctor.' He say, 'Well what are yow doing up here if you are quite well?' She say, 'Oh, I cum ter see yow about them pains I sometimes use ter git in mi boddy.' Doctor (he's Irish), he say, 'I'll mix yow up a bottle o' medisen. You mus teark a dose a' that about a quarter o' an hour before you feel tha' pains a cumen on.' Well, she went orf a thinken that one out.

Doctor say ter Aunt Agatha, 'For wiman like har, tha narstier I meark tha' medisen, tha' more good they think thas a doin 'em.'

Oh, oul Mrs.W— had a packet o' them soap powders cum bi pusst (I expect several on yer got em). She wondered if Aunt Agatha sent em tew har, if not how'd they git har nearme an address? Granfar say, 'Wi, that soap powder cum from sumone what ha' bin about here, an they ha' seen yow, an thort as how yow looked as if yow could meark good use o' that.' She scowled at Granfar.

I hev an idea Granfar is a gorne along o' our marster ter tha' show. If he dew I'll rite tew yer an tell yer how he got on.

Well, fare yer well tergether.—Yars obediently,

THE BOY JOHN.

P.S.– Aunt Agatha, she say, 'Tha's what we learn after we think we know, what count.'


## A WET SUMMER

August 31st, 1954.

Deer Sar— I hearnt rit you leartly, an I hearnt felt like a ryten. Tha whather ha' gan us orl tha blumen hump on our farm, we carnt git on wi' nurthen. Our marster dornt know wot to find us ter do, an he ount stan us orf. We shull ha' tha' harvest an tha sugar beet pullen orl mixed up tergerther. We shull be a pullen a tha' beet a tha mornen, an arter the corn in tha arternoon, wen tha' dew is orf.

Granfar say, 'I're never known a summer like this, but there yer are, that rained on St. Swiffen's, so wot ken yer expect, but as I say there allus wuss a harvest, an there allus will be a harvest.'

I dint rite about the Norfolk Show, acoss nurthen dint happen. Granfar an Aunt Agatha rid along o' our marster, sum on yer must ha' seen our marster's car, that hed a learbel on tha' windscreen.

Granfar sed tha Show wus orlrite, only that wus werry artifishel, set out more like tents in a wilderness, insted of nice grass, an big oul oak trees; they set a Show orf. When Granfar got home he say to our marster, 'I'll tell you wot, we ha' seen a good many farms today, but I hearnt seen a farm wot'll cum up to *our* farm.'

Oh, our 'Old Folkes' ha' hed an outen. Our Wicar he wus in charge. They went on a mystery drive, nobody dint know where they wore a gorne, sept the Wicar, an blowed if he dint git lorst once, that wus on a foar crorssways, wi' just a pub on tha' corner.

Granfar he wolenteered to go ter tha' pub to ask tha way. Jimmur went with 'im ter meark sure Granfar dint stop. They cum back looken werry satisfied, with the informeartion they hed fer tha Wicar.

Well, they orl got on tha way agin, an then stopped an hed dinner where there wus sum nice trees an grass, just orf tha tanpike.

They orl set roun in a ring, sept aul Mrs.W— an she set on the fence on har own, thas acos she allus meark a sloupen noise wen she eat so she dornt like eaten in company. Aunt Agatha ha' told har about it, in a nice sort a way, but Mrs.W—say, 'Thas no use, I do try eaten wi'out slupen, but then that fear to gi' me tha wind.'

Well wen they'd nearly hed their dinner, Mrs.W— she jumped, she hallered, she shook harself. Granfar thort she wus a heven a fit. Aunt Agatha, an sum more leardies, run over an see tew 'er.

Wen they found out, that feared as if she 'ed bin a seten on a warsps' nearst. Jimmur say, 'I wonder where she got stung.' Granfar say, 'I dornt know, but by how she wus a shearpen harself, I recon she'll heter stan up to hev har tea.'

Well, fear yer well tergerther.— Yars obediently,

THE BOY JOHN.


P.S.– Aunt Agatha she say, 'If you are hard up, do without a few things our grandparents never dreamt about.'


## HARVEST THANKSGIVING

October 18th, 1954.


Deer Sar— Well, our summer wot we never hed ha' cum an gone, an we din't hev time ter git our second wind arter harvest, afore we wore amon them there oul sugar beet agin. An they're a bit o' a suck in ter year, our way, they look big on top, but when yer pull 'em they tearper down so quick. Granfar say thas acus o' tha wet summer, yer see they dif't heter go down arter tha moister.

There's one thing, tha pullen an a knocken 'em earnt too bad ter year, up to now. Thow if some o' yow Norrige chaps wuster come along o' us fer only harf a day, I lay yow a shillun yow'd git knocked up. Yow'd ha' tha back earke for a month.

Them poor rabbits what keep a dyen on our farm wi' this here mixermetootsies (I think thas tha wurd) that fear ter upset all on us, an yer see me an Granfer are so fond o' rabbit pie. But to see them poor things, thas chooked us orf properly.

We wore all dun about them Rushens a bearten tha Arsenal. Granfar say, 'I told yer all along they orter a sent Norrige City, they'd a beart 'em, acos tha further they go away from home tha better they fear ter play.'

We hed our Harvest Thanksgiven a Thursday nite. Tha church was full. Mrs.W— went (she only go when there's 'suffen on'). Afterwards Aunt Agatha say, 'What did you think o' that service?' Mrs.W— say, 'Well, tha fruit an wegtables wornt as big as larst year, more wornt tha tearters an onions, an as fer that wegtable marrer, I hed a bigger one then that in my garden.'

Oh, that remind me, Aunt Agatha say there wus a boy took some apples to church for tha Harvest Thanksgiven an he say to the Wicar: 'I're brort yow eight apples, will yow please thank mother fer twelve.'

We hed our Harvest Home, as usual, in tha barn. That wus all decorated out wi' flags an flowers. We entertained ourselves ter year. Granfar sung 'Tom Bowlen' agin; tha evenin' went a bit slow till arter ten, then everyone wanted to sing. (There wus plenty o' beer.)

Oul Mrs.W— wus fulen about, an a showen orf, an mearken harself look bigoty like, then orl o' a sudden she flopped harself on to Granfar's knees (for fulery). Well that wunt a bin so series, only Granfar had a pleart o' ice cream on his lep. Well, they took har down ter yin ind o' tha barn an screarped har down, gan Granfar another pleart o' ice cream (on a clean pleart).

When she did cum back, Granfar gan har a mobben an he finished up ber sayen, 'Yow're tha ugliest old woman in tha rume.' She say, 'Well, I can't help that, ken I?' He say, 'No, but yow could ha' stopped at home, thou.' Fare yer well tergerther.— Yars obediently,

THE BOY JOHN.


P.S.– Aunt Agatha, she say, 'If you never change your opinion, you never correct your mistakes.'


## AUNT AGATHA HAS VISITORS

November 15th, 1954.

Deer Sar— We're a hullen ourselves bodily intew it, yew know wot I mean, them there oul beet. That hearnt bin tew bad duen up till now thow we git plenty o' sluss now an agin.

Thas orl pull, knock, top, pull, knock, top, till wi' fear rite disser; anyhow, we keep a dewen, thow thas orl a jorb. Bob (he's comical) he say, 'Less teark on a couple o' rows, like a gearm o' darts, a 101 up, an double out.' Us chaps think that ed be a good idea if nex year our marster hed a ringe or tew o' pineapples, among tha beet, that ed give us a little hart o' grearce.

Sum time back Granfar sed, 'We shull hater hev a bunfire John.' So he searved up orl tha hedge trimmens, an we hed a tidy big lump. Oul Mrs.W— sent a bundle of oul clothes down. Granfar put them on (with a fork).

Arter tha bonfire we orl went indoors, an Aunt Agatha hed a nice supper ridy (she allus dew a bunfire nite). Jimmur he cum an so did oul Mrs.W—, trust har to be there. She brort Aunt Agatha a bunch o' Mickelmas dearsies (short storks), becos Aunt Agatha hed meard sum altereartions for har to one o' har rummage searl skarts.

Granfar say to Jimmur, 'Juss fancy her a bringen a' dearsies; Our garden parth is lined with 'em. I shunt be surprised if that earnt were they come from, afore she cum in.'

Oh, Aunt Agatha hed har married cousen, Hetty, an her tew children cum fer tha day larst week. They dint let us know. Hetty sed she thort that ed be a surprise for Aunt Agatha, so that wuss, an a cos being Tharsday, we hearnt got much in tha house. We arn't like yow wot live in Norridge, where yow can slip out an git suffen.

Aunt Agatha say them sort o' surprises are orlrite, if you know they're a cumen. Howsumever, she found 'em suffen.

My Aunt is one o' them women wot can meark up a dinner, even if there's narthen in tha pantry.

Wen Granfar herd we'd got company he wunt cum in ter dinner, he wornt trimmed up yer see, so Aunt Agatha took him sum breard an cheese an a cup o' cooko, an he hed it in tha shud.

What meard it wass wuss our marster hed gan us a nice mess o' fresh herren, an we lay fer heven them for our tea. We knew Granfar wunt ha' them in company, acos he hev his own method o' earten them.

Well, fore Hetty an har family went away on tha five arter five bus they hed their tea. Granfar, he trimmed his self up an hed a cup o' tea with 'em.

Well, as sune as they went, we got to wark a fryen them fresh herren (I hed ter go out an borrer a loaf o' breard). My ward, we enjoyed them there herren. Granfar he had tree, yer see he wass hungry.

Well, far yer well tergerther.— Yars obediently,

THE BOY JOHN.


P.S.– Aunt Agatha, she say, 'It's good to change your mind now and again – it keeps it clean.'

# GRANFAR AND THE APPLE PIE

December 24th, 1954.

Deer Sar— My hart them there oul sugar beet are a given us a duen tew ter year. Thas bin sluss, sluss, an nourthen only sluss; yow mi' knock, yow can't git tha mud orf on 'em. If sum o' yow Norridge peeple wore ter see us at wark among them beet, well yowd wonder however we cud stick it.

Howsumever, less fergit about them, an' think about Xmas, thas on top on us afore we know where we are.

I dornt know how yow are situearted, yar part o' tha county, but our way we hearnt got no red berries on tha Crissmass ter year. Granfar, he ha hunted high an' low fer sum, he say, 'If only we cud git a little titty bit wi' berries on ter stick inter tha top o' tha pudden, John, that 'ud be beller than nourthen.'

Aunt Agatha earnt a heven any misseltoe in tha house ter year, becoss larst year oul Mrs.W— kep a tryen to ketch Granfar under tha misseltoe, an' that din't go down werry well along o' Granfar.

Wen Aunt Agatha ask Mrs.W— to ours fer Xmas Day, Granfar gan Aunt Agatha a funny oul look, but she gan him a funnier oul look back, he knew wot she meant, he knew har word wuss law in our house.

Mrs.W— ask Aunt Agatha if she'd like har to bring har an apple pie. Aunt Agatha sed, 'No, thank yer werry much.' (I know Granfar wunt a hed nune, I tell yer why). Wen Jimmur wornt well, oul Mrs.W— meard him an apple pie. Well Granfar went down to see Jimmur, an he told Granfar about tha apple pie, in fact wot wus left on it stood on tha tearble. Granfar he hed a couple o' looks at tha crust on that pie, an wen he looked at them little marks orl roun tha edge o' tha crust ter mearke it look sorter decorated, he say to Jimmur, 'Do yow hev a look them there notches round tha edges o' that pie crust, she meard them roun there wi har false teeth, yow know she ha got one tooth missen, well yow ken see that as plain as a pike starf.'

Wen Granfar told Aunt Agatha about it she said, 'Well anyhow she meant well, Granfar.' But she tarned har hid away an' smiled. (Anyhow that chooked Jimmur orf tha rest o' that pie.) O' corse, Jimmur he'll be a cumen a Xmas Day, an we lay fer heven a good time, an' I'm sure we shull, an' o' corse we shull ha' suffen in tha house.

Aunt Agatha she meard tha pudden sum time back. She let Granfar help ter stur it ter year. If yow ken remember, he din't stur it larst year becos he hed a cold in his hid.

I wish, Sar, yow cud let my Aunt Agatha know was the best day to cum up to Norridge to dew a quiet day's shopen. She went up there fer har Xmas shopen on wot she thort 'ed be tha quietest, an' she say everyone from tha country must ha thort tha searm thing, that wus crowded.

Keep yar pecker up, Norman Low, yar team is like us among tha oul sugar beet, thas a heven a sticky time jus now. Keep yow a dewen. Us country chaps will be up there a supporten on yer a Boxen Day. (None on us ount be a rabbeten ter year.)

Well, I must knock orf, but not afore wishen yow, Sar, an' orl yar starf, an' tha hull lot on yer, a Werry Happy Xmas.

So fare yer well, tergether.— Yars obediently,

THE BOY JOHN.

P.S.– Aunt Agatha, she say, 'Don't feel sorry for yourself – feel sorry for those who have to live with you.'

## LAID LOW WITH THE 'FLU

February 11th, 1955.

Deer Sar— I thort as how yowd be glad to hear as how I ha' hed tha flew, an ha bin away from wark three weeks. I wuss abed a week, I heter hev tha doctor, an wen I got up, I dint go ter wark fer a fortnite.

My Aunt Agatha, she's an angel, she looked arter me when I wus abed, an a feelen as if I dint want nourthen. She dint say to me would yow like sum of this, or sum that, no she brort me up dainty little bits on a tray, wi' a nice white clorth on. Well, if yow lay there a feelen as if yow dint want nourthen, well, when yow saw that looked ser nice, yow feared as if yow did.

Poor Granfar, he wus werry concerned; he uster cum an set alongside o' my bed. He dint say much, and I dint want to, not then, thow he did try ter cheer me up. He say, 'Yow want to try an git more grub intew yer John, yow hearn't hed more an a hin's nose full orl day.'

Well, arter I got up agin, blowed if Aunt Agatha dint tearn up queer; she wus abed foar days, wi' a bad cold an corf. Granfar he kep orlright an he wus as good as gold, an did orl he could.

The neybors (them what worn't laid up) cum an lent a hand to me an Granfar. Yer see my Aunt Agatha is werry much respected in our willage.

One day we wore bilin sum milk wen we herd some one larf. We looked roun an there stood Aunt Agatha, at tha foot o' tha' steers in har dressen gown. She sed, 'I'd like tew hav tearken a photo o' yow tew.' Yer see, I set on a chair in front o' tha fire a holden a sorsepan o' milk. Granfar he wuss on his knees wi' his nose nearly in tha sorsepan a watchen along o' me ter see that dint bile over. (We hed hed sume bile over the day afore. We wornt a gorn to say nourthen about that, only Aunt Agatha she smelt it.) She sed she cum downsteers acos we wore so quiet so she thort there wuss suffen a matter.

Oul Mrs.W— she cum down ter see if she could lend a hand. That dint suit Granfar, but as Aunt Agatha sed, that wuss werry good o' har.

One day Mrs.W— an Granfar hed a few wards an a bit o' a set tew. Granfar say tew har, 'Now, Mrs.W— I'm marster here now, an I think you'd batter be a gorn home, else you'll find yar fire out.'

Mrs.W— recon she hed tha flew. She never hed tha flew. Hars wuss only a cold, acos tew days arter she wuss standen outside tha churchyard geart wi' a lot more wimen a garpen at a funeral o' somebody she dint even know.

Aunt Agatha say what a blessen that is a liven in a country willage, where in times o' trouble everybody help everybody.

Our doctor, whose over warked, live over two miles away, and peeple wot went arter medisen ginerally brort tree o' foar bottles back ter naybors wot wornt well. Jimmur he went arter our medisen an one nite he brort six bottles back for different people. Anyhow, we're batter now, thank yer. —

Yars obediently,

THE BOY JOHN.


P.S.– Aunt Agatha she say, 'Helpful people are always the most hopeful.'


## OLD MRS.W— COMES A CROPPER

March 14th, 1955.

Deer Sar— Well we ha' hed sum rum oul whather ter year, hearn't wi? We carnt git on wi' narthen on tha farm, we carnt git tha land ridder fer them there oul sugar beet. Jimmur say he can remember when they ploughed in tha snow in February an ploughed it out agin in Earprel.

Granfar dint teark that in. He say ter Jimmur, 'I can remember five weeks o' snow in March.' Jimmur argered he coont meark that out. Granfer hed ter tell 'im, he say: 'I mean in tha town o' March, not tha month.'

Our old folkes hed a party in tha Willage Hall larst week. Sum on 'em wot hed far ter go wore took home ber car. Aunt Agatha, she stopped behind ter lend a hand a clearen up and a warshen up. Granfar he walked, an blowed if oul Mrs.W— din't ketch him up. There wuss a good bit o' snow on tha groun. She sed, 'If yow took houl o' my arm, Granfar, I think we shud both git along a lot batter.' Granfar worn't a gorn ter hev none o' that.

Arter a time, blowed if she dint slip up. Har heels flew from under har, she went over backwards unter har hinderpart a rumen.

Now she wuss a carreyen a barsket o' stuff wot hed bin left over at tha party. There wuss mince pies, tarts, an sossige rolls, sum she hed gan her, some she bort (an, Granfar say, sum she took). Tha' barsket went one way an har hat another.

Well, Granfar hed ter help har up. He got his arms round har, and he'd juss got har unter har feet, when Jimmur cum round tha corner, Jirnmur say: 'Wot are yew tew a heven a bit o' love in tha snow, Granfar.' Granfar he tarned suffen red, an my hart he cleared orf.

Jimmur, he picked up har hat, brushed har down behind, then picked har pearstereys out o' tha snow. Then he found har slip-shews, wot she wore fer tha party. There wuss a sossige roll shoved up a tha' corner of each shew, then tarts ter fill up the shews. She told Jimmur she put them there so they shunt git crushed.

Jimmur he see har ter har geart. She arsk him if he'd like a couple o' sossige rolls. Jimmur juss sed: 'No thank yer.'

Well I're cum ter tha ind o' my noot pearper, so I'll say fare yer well tergether, tha hull lot on yer.— Yars obediently,

THE BOY JOHN.

P.S.– Aunt Agatha, she say the cost of living is always about the same – all you've got!


## GRANFAR'S LIPS ARE SEALED
May 26th, 1955.

Deer Sar— That fear tha best part o' sum time since I larst rit ter yow, dornt it? Well thas all acos we're bin bissey arter them there oul sugar beet. We hed tha oul tractor a warken a night. Granfar he dornt hold wi that night wark, he say: 'Git yar land tarned over ber daylight, then them crows, an gulls, an starlens can clear tha land o' some o' tha warmen.'

Tha oul beet are a-cumen up fair to midlen, we ha' hosshowed sum on em (wi' tha tractor). Our farm is mostly hearvy land, so as our marster say, 'If we can git a plant, we can git a crop.'

Well, this Election earnt a mearken a lot o' diffus tew us, not in our willage. We ha' hed two meetens, an that fear as if one lot say one thing, an tha other lot say another. Granfar an Jimmur they talk about tha Election, but they dornt arger like they use tew, they ginerally finish up ber Granfar a sayen. 'Well, they're all alike – less gorn hev a harf-pint, Jimmur.'

Aunt Agatha hed a slight releartion o' hars call an see har tha other arternoon; he biked over, so she hed ter ask him ter tea. Granfar dint think much o' that, acos he's a chap wot dornt like wark, so o' corse he can tork a lot (there's some in every willage). As Granfar say, 'He'd tork tha hind leg orf a dickey.'

Well, this chap said he thort he'd come out an see how things wore agorn regarden tha Election in tha country willages (he live at Catton).

Well, as Granfar say, 'There is a gentleman a dewen that now, an thas Jonathan Mardle, and if he wuss a-putten up, he's tha chap I'd wote for; he write more common sense than orl them others put tergerther.'

Well, that chap went down ter tha Crown to give 'em some of his 'know', an talk about tha Election, an hear wot they'd got ter say, but he coont git a gorne. Granfar say tha converseartion wus mostly about sugar beet, gardenen, and tha frorst a-cutten orf tha arly teartes, about tha big fight an tha whather, so he never got a 'mow in' there, an he hed ter pay fer his beer.

Mrs.W—, she went ter both meetens here, an she come away none tha wiser. She say, 'Accorden to what they say, they're both right.' She say, 'Who are yo a-gorne to wote for, Granfar?' He went all high brow, he say, 'Tha ballot is secret – and now, Mrs.W—, if yow'd a hed a conshens, you could a woted accordenly to that.'

When she'd gone, Aunt Agatha told Granfar he shunt be so cantankeres to Mrs.W—. Granfar say, 'Well, she git on my narves. I lay yow a shillun that oul gal ha got a parst.'

O' corse, when tha Election is over, Mrs.W— is sure to say, 'I woted fer tha one wot got in; did yow, Granfar?' He'll give har tha searm answer he did afore – 'Tha ballot is secret.'

Well, as I sed once afore, 'Wote early, an git it over.' Fare yer well tergerther.— Yars obediently,

THE BOY JOHN.

P.S.– Aunt Agatha, she say, 'A man who can't smile, shouldn't keep a shop.'


## AUNT AGATHA'S PARTY

August 16th,1955.

Deer Sar— I know I hearnt rit leartly, well, some on yer hearnt missed much, acoss I know a hull lot on yer doarnt read yar pearper so much in tha summer as what yow do in tha winter.

I know yow go tru tha births and deaths, an tha main items an tha pictures, an hearnt them pictures bin good?

Well, tha oul beet are a looken fairly well, they want some rain, ter swell 'em out a bit. For meself, I want ter see a good crop, but I dorn't want 'em ter git tew big, do they hully teark some knocken. Our corn crops look wonderfully well.

Oh, yow know Jonathan Mardle hed a week on tha Broads. Well, I went along to Hickling wi' our marster, who knew him ter see to. Well, Jonathan Mardle wornt a bit like what I thort he wuss like. He hearnt got no trousers on (he'd got sum shorts on), an he looked an torked juss like a yotten gentleman. He wuss a carreyen a quart bottle wot said 'Cyder' On tha learble. I wonder wot wuss in it?

Granfar an Jimmur, they went an hed a look at Bob. He was a-mowen our churchyard. Someone rit ter yar pearper about tha churchyards a looken untidey on account o' tha long grass. Well, yer see, if tha grass wuss cut too soon, that 'ed grow agin an het ter be cut agin learter, an that 'ed corst a lot o' money, what most churches hearnt got, so they meark one mowen dew.

When they wi' there they hed a look roun tha tumestones, an a reeden wot wuss on 'em. Jimmur say ter Granfar, 'There dornt look as if there ha bin any sinners buried in our churchyard.' Then there wuss a plearce where tha wall wuss brooken down. Granfer say, 'That look as if that wall want a bit o' duen tew.' Jimmur say, 'I dornt know, them wot are inside cant git out, an them wot are outside dornt want ter git in.'

Oh, Aunt Agatha, she hed a birthday party, last Monday, an that wuss washen day, there wuss a good dry out an she'd finished ber tha forenoon. Mrs.W— cum. Granfar dornt like har acumen to ours on a Monday mornen acos she allus meark gearme a' his nightshat a hangen on tha line, an that meark him savidge. He carnt answer her like he'd like tew acos Aunt Agatha is allus there. Jimmur, he cum.

My Aunt Agatha ount say how old she is, thow Mrs.W— try to find out. Granfar, he know, but he dornt say nourthen. Aunt say to Mrs.W—, 'The best ten years of a woman's life are between the age of 28 and 30.' Mrs.W—, she coont meark much out o' that. She hed har teeth in far tha party; she allus hev them in fer weddens, funerals, outens an parties. Well, bor, she got in tha marster muddle wi' them teeth. She hed sum o' my Aunt Agatha's home-meard rarsberry jam, well them there pips got under har plearts. She corfed, she splattered, she werry near chooked (Granfar larfed). Aunt Agatha meard har leave tha tearble an sent har inter tha scullery, where she warshed 'em an wrapped 'em up in har hankerchief, put 'em inter har pocket, then cum back an finished har tea. Learter on we hed sum port wine, an birthday kearke. Jimmur (fer a bit o' fulery) see oul Mrs.W— home. He walked alongside on 'er, acos yer see that wornt dark. That just mused Granfar.

Well, tha days begin ter pull in, an that git leart sooner o' a night now, so I shull hev a chance to write more orfen, so, fare yer well, tergather.— Yars obediently,

THE BOY JOHN.


P.S.– Aunt Agatha, she say, 'Churchyards are full of people the world coont do without.'

## MRS.W— GOES SHOPPING

December 24th, 1955.

Deer Sar— As Granfar say, 'Here's Xmas on top on us afore we know where we are.' Do you know what? We ha' got all our oul sugar beet up out o' tha groun; yis tha hull lot on em. We hed a nice crop, an fine whathar, that wus good duin, we dint hev none o' them greart oul solers like we did lars year.

Well, thas enuff about them blumen oul beet. What about Norridge City a bearten a Brighton? That was a rumen, wornt it?

Oh, did you see in tha pearper where that sed as how they were a betten 1000 ter 1 aginst Norridge a bearten Sunderland? Hold yow hard, yow wait an see.

That remind me of a tearle Jimmur told us. He sed years ago, two chaps wore a heven a scrap outside tha Crown. One wus a big fellar, an the other one a little titty chap. Some one sed, 'Go for him little 'en, tha bigger tha man, tha better tha mark.' An that apply to Norridge City, dornt it?

O' corse, I shant go ter Sunderland, but I shull come up to Norridge an see tha replay. Can any o' yow Norridge people tell my Aunt Agatha was tha best day ter come up ter yar city fer a quiet day's shoppen? She ha tried all days an tha plearce allus fear crowded.

She took Mrs.W— up there lars week; they went a shoppen. Aunt Agatha told Mrs.W— she'd buy har suffen fer Xmas. Mrs.W— sed she'd like a pair o' shews. Well they went inter a shew shop an Mrs.W— tried on nearly every pair o' shews in tha shop (yer see har feet are awkward, she ha' got bunions).

Well, arter harf an hour she decided on a pair, an tha leardy wus a wrappen on em up fer har when Mrs.W— say to my Aunt, 'I think now praps I'd rather hev an umbrella.' Aunt Agatha say, 'No yow ount, them shews are bought fer yow, an paid for.'

Oh, Aunt Agatha say, why dornt they hev more chairs in tha shops, fer customers ter set on. She say yow trearp about Norridge orl day, an yow git tired afor yow git harf yer want. Yow could hev a notice on tha back o' tha chairs sayen, 'For elderly people only,' that would keep some o' tha young ens from a setten on em (an some o' tha older ones tew).

They both cum home from Norridge on tha bus, tired out. Mrs.W— she took har shews orf acos har feet wore unearsy. Well, when tha bus pulled up she coont find one o' har shews. Well all tha people on tha bus wore a hunten fer har shew. Tha driver shouted to tha conducter, 'What's tha matter?' Tha conducter (he wus a jolly chap) he sed, 'They're playen a Xmas gearme "Hunt tha slipper," an as soon as they hey found it we'll hev "Kiss in tha ring" an then we're orf.'

Aunt Agatha coont keep us from larfen, but Mrs.W— wus suffen savidge, har fearce wus as red as a brick, an yer see what meard it wuss, she hed a great hole in tha toe o' har stocken. When they got indoors, Granfar hed a look at Mrs.W—'s red fearce, he say, 'What ha' yow bin on tha booze missus?' She gan him a funny oul look, but never spook, so he never answered har.

Well we're all set fer Xmas. Granfar ha' got a nice lot o' Chrismas in tha shud all riddy ter put up on Xmas Eve, there plenty a berries on ter year. Granfar ha' got his bottle o' rum (he's werry partial ter rum). Aunt Agatha ha' got har bottle o' port wine, an our marster is also given on us a brearce o' fesants fer Xmas, so we ount want ter buy a chicken.

Oh, Aunt Agatha ha' hed a catasterfra. When she go ter go ter bed tha other night she found har hot warter bottle hed burst. So I hed ter go an sleep along o' Granfar an Aunt Agatha slep in my bed.

Granfar say to me, 'John, I'm plearsed that hot warter bottle hed bursted, that ha' give me an idea; me an yow will buy yar Aunt one fer Xmas.' So thas wot we're a duin on.

Well, here's me an Aunt Agatha an Granfar once agin a wishen yow, Sar, an orl yar Starf wot wark at 'Pickles', London Street, an all yow wot are a-readen this, a Merry Xmas an a Happy New.

So, fare yer well tergather.— Yars obediently,

THE BOY JOHN.

P.S.– Aunt Agatha, she say, 'A threepenny bit earnt so good as a sixpence, although it goes to church more often.'


## GRANFAR PUTS HIS FOOT IN IT

April 14th, 1956.

Deer Sar— Plearse dornt yow mob me acos I hearnt rit yow leartly, tha's acos I're bin moderate for tha best part o' sum time. I ha' bin at wark orf an on since Xmas. I heter hev tha Doctor. He gan me some narsty medicen. I believe they think, yow know, that tha narstier that tearst, tha more good that'll dew yer. He's given me injections now, so I git better sooner.

Granfar he ha' bin a keepin fit, only he ha' hed cramp, in bed. But he ha' cured that, I'll tell yow how. He say, 'When you teark yar shews orf afore you go to bed, stan em side by side, only mock em stan one shoe one way, an one tha tother, heel an toe tergether.'

He say, 'Agin, if you want to hev some good luck for tha day, when yow put yar shews on a' tha' mornen, put tha' left shew on furst, then you'll be orlrite fer tha' day.'

Well, thank goodness, my Aunt ha' finished a spring cleanen. My hart that jorb upset a home, an as Granfar say, that dornt look no different when tha's

93

done. My Aunt Agatha think that dew, but I know, an Granfar, he know, our home allus look clean, an tidy.

Oh, Granfar an Mrs. W— hed one set-tew. Mrs. W— wuss a helpen my Aunt Agatha ter spring clean. Just as Mrs. W— wuss a tearken a pail o' whitewarsh trew our rume, tew tha scullery, tha Wicar called. Mrs. W— shoved tha pail o' whitewarsh on tha' stairs, an shut tha stairs door right quick.

Well, that would a bin orlrite, only Granfar, he'd laid in a bit leart that mornen. He wuss a cumen downstairs backwards, acos he's a gitten on, and blowed if he dint plump his hinder foot right inter that pail of whitewarsh.

Bor, he hallered, He sed a bad word, tha Wicar nearly heard him. I dussent say what tha bad word wuss, but thet hed suffen ter do with a breeze o' wind.

Aunt Agatha she soon delt wi' tha situaweartion. She say to Mrs. W— 'You go an git on a white warshen tha scullery, an shut tha door. Granfar, tarn yow round an set down, dornt yow walk upstairs yit, dew you'll whitewarsh tha' whole stair carpet.'

Well she warshed his foot, an he went up an put some more trowsers on, but my Aunt kep them tew apart fer tha rest o' tha day.

Well after tha spring cleanen my Aunt Agatha took Mrs. W— up ter Norridge, an they went ter tha posh new shop wuss just opened. Poor Mrs. W— had a calamity there. That wuss on them moven stairs. They wore a gorn up ter tha' next floor. She follered Aunt Agatha, but harf way up she got tha wind up, she cum a scrappen orf down agin, a knocken people about wot wore a gorne up. She dropped har shoppen bag, har oranges an onions wore a rollen downstairs, an yit they kep a gorne up agin.

At larst she got down agin. Har umberalar wot she stuck tew, had opened out. Some fellar what stood there sed, 'What'd yow cum down by parashute Missus?'

Well tha' starf wore werry good ter har, an they helped har to git har goods tergarther. She got orl her onions orlrite, but she lorst three oranges (yer see there wuss a lot o' kids a gorne up an down a them stairs). O' course Mrs. W— wuss upset, she told Aunt Agatha she thought a drop o' short would settle har narves, but Aunt Agatha took har ter hev a cup o' tea and she wuss soon orlrite agin.

Aunt Agatha told us orl about it when she got home, an dint Granfar larf!

Well, fare yer well tergethar.— Yours obediently,

THE BOY JOHN.

P.S.– Aunt Agatha, she say, 'It's far better for us to like what we have, than to have what we like.'

# WEEDING 'EM OUT AT THE DOCTOR'S

May 14th, 1956.

Deer Sar— Thank yow fer yar kind wishes. I'm a gitten on, but I arn't right right, not yit. I shull heter keep a duen.

Them oul beet are a cummen up sorter patchy. As Granfar say, 'If we'd a hed them warm refreshen rains, wot we useter git in Earpril, them oul beet would ha' bin cut out long afore now.' How many times have I heard our marster say, when we wanted rain, 'Look at that sky over Norridge way, John, thas a rainen like billyo unter their bricks an mortar, an here's my beet a garpen fer some moisture.'

Mrs.W— she come to ours tha tother day, juss for a mardle. My aunt wuss a knitten a garment for har neece's bearby. Mrs.W— say, 'Talking about bearbies, an their mothers, there's an old sayen, *The hand that rock tha creardle rule tha world.* Aunt Agatha say, 'That wuss true years ago. Nowadays, the hand that rock tha creardle is a gitten a half-a-crown an hour – a bearby setter.'

Mrs.W— she hev some money sent har now an agin, from har sister wuss fairly well orf. Well Mrs.W— ask my Aunt Agatha if she'd go along o' har to Norridge to chuse a new custume.

Well that wuss orl a jorb. Yer see Mrs.W— she ha got wide shoulders an she's orl tha way down alike, so she's a werry orkard shearpe to fit.

Well, she got rigged up in the finish. Aunt Agatha say to har, 'Well, what about a new hat fer Whitsun?' Mrs.W— say, 'No, I hev got a new hat.' My Aunt Agatha knew all tha time that Mrs.W— ha got scores o' hats a'toom, wot she bought at rummidge searles, an she's sure ter rig one up out o' that lot wi' flowers an feathers.

Granfar say, 'Oul Mrs.W— never go nowhere a Sundays, but I lay yow a shillun she'll go ter church, an chapel an orl, a' Whit-Sunday a showen orf har new rigout an har flower show hat.

Oh, I must tell yer suffen wot happened.

Our Doctor, he's a fine man, he meark yer fear better, if he only come an see yer, an thas afore he gi' yer any medesen.

Now he told my Aunt Agatha this. (He think tha world o' har. She often help him with ould peeple wot arnt well.) Of course Doctor git fed up wi' these here wimen what go ter his sargery, when in most cearses there earnt really northen tha' matter with 'em.

Well, one mornen Doctor looked inter his waiten rume, an there they set, seven wimen (all his 'reglars'), an one man.

He sed to 'em all, 'Now this mornen I'm a' gorne to give you all a thorough examineartion an see wot really is tha' matter, wi' tha' hull lot on yer. I'll teark this gentleman first, an yow leardies can be a unloosernen, and gitten fit.'

Well, oul Mrs.W— an har pal shot out right away. Mrs.W— say, 'I dint come here prepared fer no examineartion, neither wi' mi clothes, an yit mi feet.' Her pal say, 'More dint I.'

Well, that fellar hearnt bin in that sargery many minutes afore he gan such a yell. He halered out, 'Oh, Doctor, you're a haatten me, you're a killen me.' You could a herd him down ter tha Crown.

Well, four o' them wimen shot outer that waiten rume an never stopped till they got unter tha high rood, then they started a duen up what they started unduen.

When Doctor looked inter his waiten rume, there set just one oul leardy, bolt upright, a holden her medesen bottle. That tarned out, she was stone deaf. Of corse that man what the Doctor called in first, wuss a pal of his, that wuss a put up jorb. Anyhow that worked all right, becos tha Doctor ha' hed werry few 'reglars' leartly.

Well, once agin, fare yer well tergather.— Yars obediently,

THE BOY JOHN.


## BETTER'N THAT OUL SEWERAGE CANAL

October 13th, 1956.

Deer Sar— Plearse dornt yow mob me acoss I hearnt rit leartly. Them wot know me ha' got under me a rumen acoss I hearnt hed a latter in leartly. Well tha' fact o' tha matter is, I dornt feel right up ter tha mark, not yit. Howsomever, my Aunt say I must persaware an rite more orfen, acoss, she say, she know my latters do give a lot o' pleasure to a lot o' peeple, so I shull be a doen some good, an Granfar, he say, 'John, bor, thow yar latters are a lot o' squit, they are amusen, an help to cheer up a lot o' peeple. Thas more than wot readen about that oul Sewerage Canal do.'

Oh, I had a surprise about a month ago. A leardy an her husben come right away from Wymondham a purpose to thank me for my latters ter yar pearper. She sed she wuss a Norfolk woman bred an born. She wuss on a holiday from Canada, where she'd bin saveral year, an she meard up har mind she'd visit me (an Norridge Museum). She sed she lived in a town in Canada where saveral Norfolk peeple live, an yar pearper wi' my latter in git handed all roun for them ter read. Thas a rumen earnt it? All that way orf.

Well thas enuff about me. What about our summer? You only knew that wuss August by a looken at tha almanack. Granfar say, 'Tha's them oul atom bombs wuss upset tha' wather.' Jimmur say, 'No, tha trouble wuss we hed tre munes come in wrong, we cud a done wi' out them blumen munes.' Agin Jimmur say, 'Never mind, praps we shall git two summers nex year.'

Harvest wuss a worryen time ter year, but we got trew, somehow. Granfar say, 'Yer know, John, wi' all these modern fearks on tha farm an these here combineartions wot cut an troursh, yow dornt git trew harvest as quick as we did years ago.'

O' corse, up ter now we ha' hed good wather fer gitten up tha oul sugar beet (but thas still hard wark). If the bottoms were as big as tha tops look we should ha hed some oul solers, but there yer are, we ha got a fair good crop.

Old Mrs.W— ha bin a helpen Aunt Agatha to gather har earten apples. Wen they cum indoors, Mrs.W— (who'd bin a cutten them apples inter har) say to my Aunt, 'My word, I ha' got tha belly eark.' Aunt Agatha say ter har, 'Dornt say belly, that soun ser wulgar; say stummick.'

Arter she'd gone, Granfar say ter Aunt Agatha, 'Yer know, in tha 'Eastern Daily Press' a few weeks back that sed belly wuss tha proper word, an that pearper can't be wulgar. Besides, I allus fear just as bad whither I git tha stummick eark or tha belly eark.'

I think Granfar thought he got one home then, anyhow Aunt Agatha never sed northen.

Oh, I must tell you about Mrs.W—. Last week she an Aunt Agatha went to Norridge, an after they'd finished their shoppen they went ter that Trades Exhibition at St. Andrew's Hall. Well, after a time my Aunt missed her till that wuss nearly time to catch the bus. When they met Mrs.W— sed she'd spent most o' her time round a stand were a well known Norridge firm were given away cups o' tea. She told my Aunt she'd hed seven cups o' tea fer nowthern. (Thas har all over, suffen fer nowthern.)

My Aunt wuss annoyed wi her, she say, 'You orter be ashamed o' yarself, an you know we ha got over an hour's ride home on the bus.' When my Aunt told Granfar about it he say 'Sarve her right.'

Well, fare yer well tergether.— Yars obediently,

THE BOY JOHN.

P.S.– Aunt Agatha she say, 'A woman can never keep a secret, unless she gets a few friends to help her.'


## AUNT AGATHA MAKES A CAKE

December 24th, 1956.

Deer Sar— As Granfar say, 'Here's Xmas on top on us agin, afore we know where we are. Now I tell yow what, yow aren't a gorn ter hear much about them there owl sugar beet, not this time. We ha' got tha' best part o' most on 'em up. We ha hed pretty good duen, but thas hard work even in fine weather.

Thas a rum oul world nowadays, earnt it? Thas a job when yer think on it, when we ha' got ter export Jonathan Mardle ter America (I suppose thas to searve dollars). I hope he'll soon be back an I hope Adrian Bell ount hev ter go, acos Granfar he enjoy a readen wot them two wright, in yar pearper. He say they do know what they write about, an he can understand it.

Aunt Agatha, she ha' meard her Xmas keark. She allus worry about whither thas a gorn ter tarn out all right, but that allus do. She meard a tearster, an that wuss luvely.

Mrs.W— she meard a keark tew. Aunt Agatha went down ter hers just afore she put it inter her tin.

My Aunt say, 'My heart that smell suffen strong, what did yow flavour that with?'

Mrs.W— say, 'I put in what wuss in that little bottle with a "P" on it, I think thas pineapple.'

Aunt Agatha hed a look, she say 'That earnt pineapple thas peppermint.' When Aunt Agatha told Granfar, my hart he larfed, he said 'That ount do her no harm, she suffer from wind.'

Aunt Agatha say, 'She is sure to bring a piece down here, an you musn't hart har feelens, you must hev sum, an tell har how nice it is, that'll plearse har a rummen.'

Granfar say, 'If I must hev a piece, I'll hev just a titty little bit, an spit it out arter she's gone.'

Mrs.W— went along o' my Aunt ter Norridge, ter do ther Xmas shoppen, an earnt shoppen a jorb in yar City? – Push an shuv, orl tha time.

Well, that wuss a gitten nigh bus time, Mrs.W— she wandered orf on har own, up ter tha top ind o' yar Market plearce, an blowed if she wornt robbed.

She told Aunt Agatha she wuss a listenen to a gentleman who could hully talk. She sed he was ever so nice, he sold her suffen for 1s. 9d. wot he ask 5s. 6d. for fer a start. She took her purse out o' tha top o' har shoppen bag, what wuss full, gan him harf a crown an he give har har change.

When she go ter put har change inter har purse a top o' har bag, there wus har purse – gone! Oh she was upset. When she met my Aunt Agatha, she wuss full on it.

However, my Aunt found out that there was only 1s. 3d. in her old purse, that wornt so bad, only her bus ticket wuss in har purse tew.

When the conductor on the bus (what wuss crowded) ask Mrs.W— fer har ticket she started tellen him all about her bein robbed. He say, 'I hearnt got time to hear all that rig-mer-roll now Missus, I'll come back learter.' Anyhow Aunt Agatha meard things right with tha conductor.

Well, I think we ha' got everything 'laid on' orlright fer Xmas. We're heven chicken ter year an o' corse we're got suffen in the house. We're heven a Xmas party an I'll wright an tell yer how we git on.

Once agin me an Aunt Agatha an Granfar wish yow an yar starf, an orl yow what read this, a werry Happy Xmas.

So fare yer well tergether, tha hull lot on yer.— Yars obediently,

THE BOY JOHN.

P.S.– Aunt Agatha, she say, 'Tact is making your company feel at home even though you wish they were.'


## HOW MRS.W— GOT A NEW HAT

February 2nd, 1957.

Deer Sar— Well, they're bin gone away best part o' some time now – them oul sugar beet I mean – an we ha bin gitten tha' land riddy ter sow some more. That ha' bin pretty good duen ter year, the wather ha' bin kind tew us, an we ha' hed a good crop.

I asked our marster how they'd tarned out, he say, 'Not ser bad John, not ser bad.' Now when a Norfick farmer say 'not ser bad', that mean jolly good.

Oh, Granfar he ha bin kinder moderate leartly, thow he's better now. Jimmur, he went up ter tha doctor's, an fetched him a bottle o' fissic. Jimmur say tha doctor ha' got a nootis a hangen up in his waiten roum, that say 'No talken please, an hev yer symptons riddy.' Doctor told Jimmur them there women git tergather, an talk to each other about their complaints so much, that when they git inter tha' surgery they don't know who ha got what.

A cumen out o' tha surgery, Jimmur met Ben, then a gorne in, he say, 'Wass up wi' you Ben?' Ben say, 'I're ha' got lumbeargo, a rumen.' Jimmur say, 'Thas no use a you a-gorn ter see tha' doctor fer that, he ha' hed lumbeargo for a week, an tha's a sure moral, if he can't cure his self, he can't cure you.'

When Jimmur come back wi' tha medisen, Granfar got tha rum bottle out an they hed a drop apiece. Granfar say, 'When yer dornt fare well Jimmur tha rum dornt tearst ser nice as that do when you're all right.'

Do you know what? Oul Mrs.W— allus git inter a frap when she go up ter Norridge. My Aunt Agatha wen up ter tha shop searls, ter buy Granfar some shats, socks (I mean stockens), an underclothen. Mrs.W— she went tew, thow she dint want nourthen perticular.

Well, they went inter a big shop, an there wuss a hull pile o' women's hats on a counter. Mrs.W— she hed a look roun them, an' she fitted one on; tha leardy behind tha counter sed to Mrs.W—, 'There madam, that hat makes you look ten years younger.' Mrs, W— say, 'Well, I arn't a-gorne to hev it, 'cos when I teark it orf, I shull look ten years older.'

99

Well, my Aunt went ter another part o' tha shop ter buy what she went for, an' left Mrs.W— a-hangen round tha hats. Learter on they met near tha entrance out, an' they were walking along tha Walk when my Aunt say, 'So you bought a new hat?' Mrs.W— say, 'No, that I hearnt.' 'Well, my Aunt say, 'You're got a new hat on.' She say, 'Oh, I hearnt, hev I?'

Then Mrs.W— looked at harself in a shop winder what shined. She say, 'Oh dear, what ever shull a do? They're sure ter summons me fer stealen.' They both went back ter tha shop agin, an my Aunt explained what hed happened ter tha leardy in charge o' tha hats, an she wuss werry nice about it, she could see that my Aunt wuss ever so respectable.

O' corse Mrs.W— she wuss proper flabbergasted, she'd got a red fearce, an' looked ever ser guilty.

They hunted trew them hats fer Mrs.W—'s oul hat, but they coont find it. Then the gentleman wass in charge o' the shop come along, an' when he herd what hed happened, he wuss werry nice. He say ter Mrs.W—, 'We understand that it's a genuine mistake, madam, will you please accept tha new hat as a gift from us?'

Cumen out o' tha shop Mrs.W— say, 'Do you think we oughter learve my nearm an' address, so if they find my hat they can pust it on ter me?'

My Aunt say, 'No, yow let things be as they are, yow hearn't done ser bad.'

When Granfar herd about it he say, 'There yer are John, if yar Aunt hearn't a-bin along o' har, that oul gal would a bin in Norridge jail ter night.'

Well, fare yer well tergather.— Yars obediently,

THE BOY JOHN.


P.S.– Aunt Agatha, she say, 'I don't like to repeat gossip – but what else can yer do with it?'


## THE OLD FOLK'S PARTY

March 11th, 1957.


Deer Sar— Well, we're a gitten trew tha winter pritty well, an we ha' got most o' tha land riddy fer them oul sugar beet agin. Yisterday we drilled tha oul ten earkers wi' oats an Granfar say he never see tha wheats look bettar. Hearnt tha birds bin a singen ever ser luvely since Christmas? Aunt Agatha say they're a tellen tha world how beautiful it is. Granfar say, 'Yis, but they wunt do that if they could read tha newspearpers.'

Granfar, he wuss up arly, that furst o' March, he got tha' oul brume out an swep tha fleas orf tha door step (searm as he allus hev done).

He wuss up arly agin Shrove Tuesday. He got forrard wi all his odd jobs, trimmed hiself up an he an Jimmur went orf down ter tha Crown fer a couple o' harf pints, as Granfar say, 'A keepen up tha' oul custum.' Yer see, years ago, chaps on the farm allus hed a half day's holiday on a Shrove Tuesday, an so did tha sckule children, and there wuss allus a plowin match, mostly fer a leg o' pork, o' corse thas all done away with now.

When they come back to ours, tha Doctor wuss there. He'd come ter see my Aunt about gitten an oul leardy inter tha hospital. Granfar he's like a lot more people, when ever they come acros tha' Doctor (outer surgery hours) they allus remember there's suffen tha matter with 'em. Granfar say, 'Doctor, I suffer from inderjestion.' Doctor, he looked at Granfar and sed, 'Well Granfather, what's better than a pint of hot water after each meal?' Granfar say 'Inderjestion.'

Well, bein Panceark Day, Jimmur hed his dinner along wi' us as usual. Oul Mrs.W—, o' corse, she come tew, an as long as that wuss pancearks she never hed har false teeth in. Granfar say ter Jimmur, 'When she set there a chowen, har chin an har nose nearly meet tergather.' (Only he dint say nose.) Granfar, he eart four pancearks. My Aunt allus meark tha last one wi' currans in.

After dinner Granfar an Jimmur, they rested. Granfar say, 'I're got some pain o' my stumick, Jimmur.' Jimmur say, 'I dornt wonder, yer know yar stumick is like a Parish Council, Granfar. When tha's a worken properly, yow dornt know you're got it.'

At four o'clock, orf we all went ter tha Old Folk's party. Mrs.W—, she went. She recon she earnt old enough ter join, but Aunt Agatha know better.

Mrs.W—, she go as a washer-up. She dornt git no pay, she juss git wuss left over afterwards, as Granfar say. She dornt lose northern by that. He recon by what she hev gan tew her, an what she scrounge, she werry orfen want a barrer ter git tha stuff home.

They hed a luvely tea, ice cream an all, then afterwards a leardy sung five songs. After that they enjoyed theirselves. They had all sorts o' gearms, an they got Granfar ter sing. He sung 'Tom Bowlen,' thas tha only song he know. Bob, he's 84, he did a step dance. Fred (79), he played his concertena fer Bob ter dance tew. Mrs.W— she put her spoke in where that wornt wanted. As Granfar say, 'She's biggoty.' She said, 'Why not hev kissen in tha ring?'

Granfar scowled, but nobody else spook.

Well, they finished with their hymn, then 'Oul Lang Sine,' then 'God save tha Queen.' As Granfar sed afterwards, 'A good time wuss hed by all.' Well, fare yer well, tergarther.— Yars obediently,

THE BOY JOHN.

P.S.– Aunt Agatha, she say: 'It doesn't matter what happens, there's always someone who knew it would.'

# THE BOY JOHN IN HOSPITAL

May 20th, 1957.

Deer Sar— Thas suffen nice ter be home agin, thow I shornt be earble ter do any wark fer a long time. Tha doctor say as how I're got ter preserve my strength. Granfar, he cleaned an sharpened an iled my hoe riddy fer them oul sugar beet, but there yer are, they'll heter git on wi' out me ter year.

Our marster he drive me an Granfar rown tha farm, an all tha crops look pretty good, but Granfar he say no crops ount be ever so good ter year, acoss tha land missed them frorsts what we dint git larst winter. Granfar's tearters dint miss that frorst we got tha t' other night. He lorst foar rows, they wore as black as yer hat.

Well, now, just a few items about what happened at the Hospital. I hed a lot o' visitors. My Aunt Agatha came whenever she could git away. Sister Norton gan her a special pass. Our marster an missus come an see me three times, an so did Jimmur. Once when Aunt Agatha come she told me Granfar he'd bin ever so good, he'd helped har all he could, an he did all tha jobs I use ter do. She said he'd cleaned both pair o' my shews, an one day she missed him, she peeped in tha shud, an there he wus a cleanen my oul bike, an he an Jimmur hed looked arter my bit o' garden.

I muss tell yer about tha first time my Aunt Agatha brought Granfar an Mrs.W—. Granfar he did look smart, he'd got his Sunday sewt on, his hair wuss nice an tidy, an his shews hully shined. He stood alongside o tha bed for some time, then he say, 'I dornt like ter see yer like this, John bor. Meark hearst an git batter.' My Aunt cheered Granfar up a bit, an we soon got talken about things at home an on tha farm.

Mrs.W— stood back a bit. I could see she wuss a chowen suffen (I could see, tew, she'd got har teeth in – she allus put them in when she go up to Norridge). I sed ter my Aunt. 'Wass she a chowen on?' My Aunt say, 'Peppermints, she allus eat them whenever she go inter a hospital; she say they keep tha microbes away.'

Well after a time, my Aunt told Granfar to hev a walk down the Ward, so Mrs.W— could come an see me. She brought me a big bag of peppermints, a bunch of flowers (short storks) an a long brown pearper parcel all tide up, that wuss a surprise, an not to be opened till arter she wuss gone.

Well, she set harself down alongside a my bed, a torken about tha different peeple she knew what hed died in Hospital. I put my bunch o grearpes, what a leardy from Bacton hed brought me, inter my locker as soon as I caught site of Mrs.W— (she can be absent-minded).

All of a sudden we herd a commotion at yin ind o tha Ward. We looked, poor Granfar he'd tumbled down (he wornt hurt). Two nurses picked him up an they all three on em come arm in arm down o tha Ward, they wore all a larfen. Oul Mrs.W— she looked suffen savidge ter see them mearken a fuss o Granfar. She say, 'He fell down a parpus to git a little simpathy' (but he dint).

Granfar come an set alongside o my bed, and Mrs.W— went rown tha Ward an give every pearshent one a har peppermints, then she sed she'd go outside tha Ward an wait fer Granfar an my Aunt.

Well then them two said goodbye an went out inter tha corridor. When they got there, there stood Mrs.W— with har hid well up, har eyes shut an har tung out, an a hull lot of peeple a garpen at er. My Aunt spoke ter har, an brought har back ter normal.

Now this is wot hed happened. Charler, wot use ter live in our willage, he was a ward orderly in tha Hospital, so he hed a white coat on. Mrs.W— she met him an knew him. She say, 'Wi' Charler, what are yow, a Doctor?' Charler (he played up ter har – he wuss allus full o' fulery), he sed 'Yis.'

Well then she told him all her simptoms. He said, 'I'll soon cure yow, now do as I tell yer, put yar hid well back, shut yar eyes, and put yar tung out and wait till I come back' – o' corse, he never come back.

My Aunt wornt werry plearsed, but how Granfar larfed.

Arter they'd gone me an tha narse undone Mrs.W—'s mystery parcel, and what dew you think that wuss? Six sticks o' rubub. 'Rubub!' tha narse say, 'we ha got enough trouble in this Ward now.'

Well I must earse orf now, so fare yer well tergether,— Yars obediently

THE BOY JOHN.

P.S.– Aunt Agatha, she say 'Kindness is one thing you can't give away – it alaways comes back.'

## GRANFAR DRAWS A FURRER

October 26th, 1957.

Deer Sar— As Granfar say, time fear ter be a slippen away, an what wi putten tha clocks back we ha' got tha' winter on top on us afore wi know where wi are. O' corse thas orl them oul sugar beet on tha farm now, tha's nourthen only knocken, toppen, an a loaden. Thank goodness that ha' bin good doen leartly. Round our way tha crops aren't so heavy ter year an a lot on 'em ha got this oul virus.

Granfar like them pictures in yar pearper, specially them wi' tha hosses a quowen. Yer see we ha' got two hosses on our farm, Prince, an Beauty. Our marster keep them becos he's fond on 'em, an they come in handy for odd jobs.

Granfar allus go an speark to 'em every day, he think tha woorld o' them.

Tha other day tha hosses an plow went inter our long pightle. Our marster say, 'What di yer say, Granfar, would yer like ter see if yow can draw a furrer, down to yin ind and back?' Granfar say, 'Yis, I'll hev a go.'

They put a steark down for him, he collared houl or tha tail o' tha plow, an tha reams, an orf they went, Granfar gi' them plenty o' 'Kep here, halt, whoosh.' Them hosses knew him. Well, when he cum back, we had a look at his furrer, that wus as straight as a die. Worn't everyone plearsed, specially Granfar, his red fearce wuss one big smile. Our marster say, 'Come on, Granfar, yar furrer is well worth a harf pint. We'll go down ter tha Crown. Bring Jimmur wi' yer.' An' now all tha village know about Granfar's furrer.

So yow ha hed to hoist tha price o' yar pearper. Granfar say, 'There yer are, John, that pearper ha' bin comen inter this house fer tha larst forter year, an thow they ha hained it a penny, we're still a gorne to keep a tearken on it. Arter all, thas only harf a fag a day more, an' if anyone dorn't think they're a-gitten ther money's worth, well, they can read all tha advertisements as well.'

My word, dint Granfar enjoy them pictures o' them donkeys in yar pearper larst week. He looked at that picture o' that bearby donkey a-gallopen, an he larfed an he larfed an he larfed, till his specticals fell orf o' his nose. (I ha called 'em donkeys becos people what dorn't live in Norfolk dorn't know tha proper nearme is dickey.)

I know what deart it wuss, that wuss tha larst day in September. Mrs. W— come spufflen in, she was so plearsed wi' harself. She say, 'I've juss bin up ter Pust Office, and bought a dozen tuppeny hapeny stamps. Yer see, they go up ter treepence ter morrer.'

Well, me an Granfar wore a playen drafts, becos tha whurther worn't fit enough fer me ter go out. O' corse she hed ter barge in, tellen Granfar where ter muve his drafts. Well, he put up wi' that, but when she go ter put her finger on ter one o' his drafts, my hart he gan a swipe at har hand. He missed that, caught tha corner o' tha draft board, an sent tha drafts all over tha kitchen floor.

Granfar he hallered. My Aunt Agatha herd the commotion. She called Mrs. W— inter her scullery an that worn't long afore that oul gal went home. (My aunt let her out tha back way.)

Well, I let Granfar win tha nex gearm, so that cheered him up a bit. He say, 'Yer know, John, that wuss bad enough, a-heven har loken on over my shoulder a-breathen inter my ear (only he dint say ear), but she tempted to move my drafts. Well, I lorst my temper, besides she kep a sniffen. I shunt be surprised if she hearnt got this here Alsation flew.'

Well, fare yer well tergather.— Yars obediently,

THE BOY JOHN.

P.S.– Aunt Agatha, she say, 'Other people's faults are like car head lights, they seem more glaring than our own.'

# GRANFAR'S NEW PYJAMAS

November 23rd, 1957.

Deer Sar— We're got tree parts on em up an' orf tha' land (them oul sugar beet I mean). Tha whather ha' bin werry open, so we ha' got on a rumen, we ha' got all our wheart in tew.

Now you ount hear much about Mrs.W— this time, she earnt werry well, she hed to hev tha' Doctor. She's suffen plearsed acos tha' Doctor say she ha got a new complaint what ha' only bin out a month.

My Aunt Agatha hed a letter from an old friend o' hars, wot married a farmer, so o' course she's well orf now. She said: 'I'll send tha car for yer, here and back, we can hev a good oul tork tergerther. Bring Granfar an John.'

Well, when we got there they'd got telewision on so we all set an looked at that til eight a' clock, then we hed corfee, cearkes and sandwiches, then looked agin till nearly ten, then my aunt sed: 'Look at tha' time!' That wus ten a'clock, so we wook Granfar up an come hoom. When we got hoom my aunt said: 'There, John, thas what telewision do. I went there to hev a nice long chat with her. We ha' sed nothen, she'll hev to come to ours.'

My Aunt Hetty, she come an stayed at ours fer a night or tew. She allus bring us suffen. She brought me a pair o' slip shews an Granfar a pair o' thick perjarmers. They'd ha bin better if Granfar hed hed tha' shews.

Now, Aunt Hetty slep in my bedroom, an I slep in a camp bed in Granfar's roum. Well we went upstairs, Granfar he got inter them perjarmers. They hed bright stripes, he looked a jorb. He larfed, he walked up and down. He say: 'John, I fear as if I am yotten o tha Broads.'

We hearnt bin in bed long: I could hear him a jifflen about. Arter a time he say: 'Are you aweark, John? Twitch yar flash light on. Dorn't twitch on tha bedroum light, yer Aunt might see it under tha' door. Now will you plearse git my niteshat out o' tha cuberd. I can't sleep in these here pyjarms. The leg parts ha drawed up ter my knees, an they are tight roun my hinderpart. I'd be a darned site more comfortable wi' my trousers on.'

Well, I got his niteshat and he wus soon asleep. When my Aunt Hetty went away my Aunt Agatha sed: 'Granfar, I expect you'll find yer nightshat more comfortable.'

My aunt knew what hed bin gorn on, I'll tell you why. It wus tha way we folded that niteshat every mornen, we coont get it to fold neat like my aunt did. We tried to fold on the bed, then on the floor. We coont git the rucks out.

Well, far yer well tergerther.— Yars obediently,

THE BOY JOHN.

P.S.– My Aunt Agatha say, 'A secret is something you tell *one* person – at a time.'

## MRS.W— BRINGS HOME A BROOM

January 18th, 1958.

Deer Sar— My Aunt Agatha say I mustn't write a lot about myself, but I'm a little better, thankyer.

They ha' got well ahid on tha farm on account o' tha fine weather. Them oul beet wore all away afore Chrissmas, there wornt such a good crop ter year. We ha' got tew fields ploughed up all ready for next year's beet. Them fields are waiten fer tha frosts ter help breark tha soil up. Our whearts look ever so well. Granfar say they want about tree inches o' snow on 'em ter keep 'em warm. My Aunt say, 'Yow may want some snow fer your wheat, I dornt want any fer my feet, thank yer.'

Oh, Chrissmas Eve Granfar an Jimmur went down ter tha Crown fer a harfpint. They din't stop long, an when they got back they said they wore gorn inter tha shud fer a time.After a while my Aunt said, 'I wonder what they're up tew, John? They hed a guilty sort o' look on their fearces. I'm gorne to hev a peep at them.'

When she come back she wuss roaren wi' larfter. She say, 'What do yow think, John? There they set on a couple o' boxes wi' tha hurrican lamp hung over the top on 'em, an my barth in between 'em, a-plucken a duck.'

A little learter on in come them two wi' tha duck, their fearces a beamen, an their clothes covered wi' down. They presented my Aunt wi' tha duck.

Granfar, he'd won that duck in a draw at tha Crown, an they wanted to searve my Aunt tha trouble o' plucken on it. My Aunt thanked 'em an' said, 'By tha look o' yar clothes you'd better go back an' start plucken each other now.' My Aunt helped 'em, she used a damp dwile.

Jimmur and Mrs.W— come to ours Chrissmas Day (they allus do). We had a luvely dinner. Chrissmas pudden, chicken first o' corse. We hed sum buteful sorce wi' tha pudden, as Granfar say, 'That ha' got a kick in it, John.' My Aunt did things proper, we hed corfee afterwards.

Mrs.W— wuss a drinken har corfee wi' tha spune still in har cup. Granfar he twigged that. He say, 'Missus, if yow dorn't teark yar spune out o' yar cup when you're a drinken, you'll be a poken yar eye out.' She never spoke, but she took it out. She wuss suffen savidge to think that Granfar hed showed har up. Well, after we'd heard the Queen's speech we all sort o' dozed off till tea time, then nobody din't want any tea, only ter drink.

Arter tea we played cards till supper time. Granfar he wun't play. He said he had rumeatism in his hands, but I knew different ter that. Yer see he oun't play cards wi' Mrs.W—, he say she cheart.

Well, tha party broke up about 11 o' clock. Granfar got tha rum bottle out and he an Jimmur hed 'one fer tha road'. My Aunt an Mrs.W— hed a glars o' port wine each. Jimmur said he'd see Mrs.W— home. She wuss suffen

106

plearsed, so wuss Granfar.

Oh, I muss tell yer about Mrs.W— an my Aunt Agatha a-gorne up ter Norridge, just afore Chrissmas. They shopped tergether fer a time. My Aunt say Mrs.W— allus *pull* on shop doors what say *push*. (I reckon some on yer ha done tha searme, hearn't yer?)

Well they parted an met again at tha bus steartion. Mrs.W— wuss carryen a yard brume on a long handle. My Aunt said, 'Why ever din't yow hev that brume tied roun tha handle.' Mrs.W— said, 'I told tha man I coon't fix it up myself so he fitted it an screwed it on fer me.'

When she got into tha bus, tha conductor said, 'I dorn't know what yow are gorne ter dew wi' tha brume, mam, there's no rume in the back here.' Now that wuss one o' them buses where there are three seats where yow set sideways each side o' tha bus, at tha back. Well, she plonked harself down there wi' tha brume atween har feet.

Well, that wom't long afore that brume slipped out at tha foot, nearly trippen people up. Arter she hed tha conductor nearly tripped up twice, he say, 'Yow'd better turn that brume tha other way up, Missus, dorn't you'll be a brearken some one's neck.' So she put tha brume tha other way up.

Then she hed to put up with some remarks. One chap sed, 'Hello, Missus, what are yow a-expecten some snow yar way?' Another one said, 'What are yer gorne ter ride over tha mune ter night?' Another one said, 'Who are yow, mam, Britannia?'

My Aunt told Granfar that wuss a good job Mrs.W— din't loose har temper, she might ha' struck someone. Granfar say, 'I dorn't know, that would ha bin a rum job ter teark a swipe at anyone with a long-handle brume in a crowded bus.'

Poor Norridge, they struck a bad patch on Saterday. Never mind, they'll come on agin. Let me tell yow critics somethen about bein at tha top o' tha league.

> *'Tha's easier ter git there*
> *Than it is ter stick there.'*

Oh dear, tha's pust time an my Aunt earn't home yit fer har pust script. Granfar say he'll write one (please forgive him).

Fare yer well tergether.— Yars obediently,

THE BOY JOHN.

P.S.– Granfar, he say, 'If women know so much why do they ask so many questions?'

# AUNT AGATHA AT THE DOCTOR'S

March 1st, 1958.

Deer Sar— Tha days are droren out a rummen, aren't tha? We hed tea by daylight tha Sunday arter Walentine (we allus do). We hed pankearks a Shrove Tuesday, an tha's all we knew it by. Granfar sed years ago on a Shrove Tuesday, tha children allus hed a half day's holiday, an so did men on the farm, an there was allus a plowen match, mostly for a leg o' pork.

They ha got well away wi' tha wark on tha farm, our marster ha hed to find tha chaps a jorb a' trimmen a fences an cleanen out holls.

My Aunt Agatha showed us har kittle what hed furred up inside, since she ha used tha tap water. Granfar say, 'There yer are, John, if I hed a-drank tha water outer that tap instead o' outer my pump, my inside would ha bin like that kittle, all furred up.'

Our doctor went away fer a few days, so we hed another doctor. Now our doctor ask my Aunt if she would go down to tha surgery for tha first mornen, an give tha new doctor a little idea of who wuss who. He said he wuss sure that all the 'reglars' would be there to see what the new doctor wuss like. He say ter my Aunt, 'Nowadays, at tha surgery, so many come fer so little.'

Well, my Aunt set in a room alongside tha surgery, so she could see without being seen, she was so amused with one peartient who tha doctor interviewed that when she got home she rit it all out. She said, 'I think that'll do fer yar latter, John,' so I'm a-copy 'en it down, and here 'tis:

| | |
|---|---|
| *Doctor –* | Good morning, Mrs. Smith. Now what is your trouble? |
| *Mrs. Smith –* | Tha's what I're come ter see you about. |
| *Doctor –* | I see. Now do you get any pain? |
| *Mrs. S. –* | Not to say any pain, tha's bad enough without. |
| *Doctor –* | In what way do you suffer? |
| *Mrs. S. –* | Oh, I suffer suffen cronick. |
| *Doctor –* | Well now, what are you complaining about? |
| *Mrs. S. –* | Oh, I aint one ter complain, doctor. My husban say ter me at breakfas this mornen, 'Martha,' he say, 'with all yow suffer tha's a wonder yow never complain.' Oh, no, doctor. I'm not one ter complain. |
| *Doctor (now beginning to see through his patient) –* | Well, in what way do you suffer? |
| *Mrs. S. –* | Well, that start in my inside, inwardly, then that fer ter fly ter my back; that fear like a lot o' worms a knawren my backbone, an I git a lot o' wind, well yow doctor, yow know. *(After a pause)* Look, doctor, what I want is fer yow to *cure* me, all yow pear ter do is ter keep asken the questions. |

*Doctor (catching my aunt's eye, and now knowing how to deal with this patient)*
— Well, Mrs. Smith, I must send you to Norwich Hospital for a thorough examination.

*Mrs. S.* — Oh, no, no, doctor. I arn't as bad as all that. I dorn't want ter go ter no hospital, if you can give me a bottle o' medicen. I'm sure that'll put me right. I'd lik a bottle that searm colour as what yow give Mrs. Brown wass juss gone out. I've bin a torken ter har an my complaint was warse than her's. Her medicen wass clear. I'd like mine thick at tha bottom, so yow ha' got to sheark it afore yer teark it. I know that'll cure me.

Doctor he gave har a bottle as prescribed by har, she was greatly relieved. (So was the doctor.)

Granfar an Jimmur are werry pleased about their extra ten shillings a week pension money. Jimmur say he's gorn ter buy a motor cruiser an teark Granfar on tha Broads, an Granfar he's gorn ter buy a motor-car an teak Jimmur out. (Mrs.W—, she's away.)

Well, fare yer well tergerther.— Yars obediently,

THE BOY JOHN.

P.S.– Aunt Agatha, she say, 'Women love the simple things in life – MEN.'

## GRANFAR DOES A GOOD TURN

April 7th, 1958.

Deer Sar— They're gitten well away on the farm. They ha' got 12 earkers o' them oul sugar beet in, an two more fields nearly fit ter drill. Our oats an barley are sown, all we want is some fine weather.

They say 'March hek ham, in like a lion an out like a lamb.' Well that come in, an went out like a lamb, but the oul lion did a good bit o' roaren in between.

Jimmur he meard a rear feark, his snow plow, that wuss a big box lid wi' a shaft on, you shoved it ahid on yer, an that easily meard a path. Now, he wuss up arly an he cleared up roun his cottage, that wuss tha mornen when we hed all that snow.

Then he come on down to ours. He pulled up at Mrs.W—'s cottage, he see she wuss bunged up wi' snow an he soon cleared a parth from har door ter tha garden geart. Then he meard a parth ter tha coal shud, an another little plearse (he could see by har footmarks she bin tryen ter git there, but hed ter tarn back).

Well, she ask him ter come in an hev a cup o' tea. He said, 'No thank yer, I oun't come in' (yer see he wuss afraid tha neybors might talk) so he hed a cup o' tea an tew short kearks outside, then cum on to ours.

He an Granfar soon cleared up roun ours, then they heard there wuss a bus stuck in a drift up o' tha road. Jimmur said, 'Come on, Granfar, bring yer shovel, less see if we can lend a hand.' Off they went, but after a lot o' hard work, they found tha bus coon't quite help harself out.

Granfar see there wuss about a dozen people in tha bus, includen a Wicar (not our Wicar). He put his hid inside tha bus an sed, 'Now then tergerther, you'll ha' ter try an help yarselves outer this muddle. If you all come out an push behind I think that will juss do tha jorb. If not yow'll set there an freeze ter death afore tha thaw set in.'

Out they come, looken properly fed up. Granfar got 'em all shoven behind. At tha second push, tha oul bus fairly jumped out unter tha road agin, an tha hull lot o' tha pushers fell down in a lump in tha snow. Someone swore, but Jimmur said he din't think tha Wicar herd, becoss his ears wore bunged up wi' snow. When they were picken theirselves up, one on 'em bust out a-larfen, then tha hull lot on 'em were larfen, they could see tha funny side.

Well, they brushed each other down an got inter tha bus agin. They got outer that bus like a funeral party, an got back in agin as happy as sand boys. Granfar say that juss show yer how a calamity can bring people tergerther.

They nearly all gan Granfar an Jimmur a tip – Three an tenpence alltergerther. Jimmur say, 'I think we deserve harf a pint. I'll show yer how ter git one fer nourthern. Bring yer shovell, we'll go down ter tha Crown.'

Orf they went. They never went in. They got ter wark wi their shovels, they cleared all tha snow away in front o' tha pub an meard a parth up ter tha road, then went in an ordered two harf pints. Tha landlord sed, 'You're a couple a' good fellars, yow'll hev two harfpints along o' me, two harfpints o' my best old beer.'

They hed a good warm up and when they got home my Aunt say, 'You're got rare red fearces.' Granfar sed, 'Yis, we hed a hid wind all the way home; we helped to git tha bus outer a snow drift.' My Aunt say, 'You smell as if it wuss a brew-cart wot got stuck.' Jimmur winked at Granfar, he tried ter wink back.

Oul Mrs.W—, she wuss down to ours, full o' earkes an pains. She reckon she'd ha' ter go an see tha doctor in tha mornen.

Granfar say, 'Three parts o' yow women trouble tha doctor when yow could cure yarself at home. You wanter do tha searme as I allus do at home when I dorn't feel well, thas tearke a good oul dose o' Epsom salts in tha mornen, an a bearsen o' biled onions at night. If that ount cure yer, well, that will stop yer from botheren tha doctor for a day or tew.

Well, fare yer well, tergerther, I sharn't see yer at Tombland ter year.

Yars obediently,

THE BOY JOHN.

P.S.– Aunt Agatha, she say, 'Work is a cure for grumbling. Even a mule can't kick when he's pulling.'

# A COUNTRY FUNERAL

It was one of those warm, sunny days with which this year has suddenly burst straight out of winter into summer. The fields and hedges were green, and the hawthorn in flower, but most of the trees were still bare, as if dubious, after so many weeks of biting winds, of breaking even yet into leaf. In the brown copses, only the larch was gloriously green. But as we rode down into the flat Broads country, the landscape was already dotted with white and red sails.

It was a day so glad with the evidence of resurrection that it was not possible to feel unhappy about death. We came at length to the village that had been made by the holiday traffic – big new boathouses, big new stores, big red pub. But the church was not there. We went a mile up a side road, winding between hedges, until we came to the old village that was still agricultural. We could hear the bell tolling across the bright fields where the corn was young and the birds were singing.

Then we saw the church, with a roof of silvery-brown reeds from the Broad, and a round flint tower that the villagers must have built under the direction of monks, nine hundred years ago, out of stones carted up from the beach, when this parish was an island of farm land in the midst of undrained fen, meres and salt creeks, and the heathen Danes had but lately ceased from plundering.

Now the rough triangle of grass outside the church was surrounded with motor cars, and from them people walked slowly in the sunshine, through the churchyard, into the porch surmounted by a crude stone carving of a man with a club. The effigy may have been a pagan figure of a green man, a spirit of the woods, but long ago, when it was dug up from the ground, the parish thought it was a figure of a Christian saint, and hallowed it, and set it above the porch.

We went into the church, and found it full of people, and decorated with flowers as if for a festival. The sun poured in through the wide windows of the aisle, and, from high windows in the clerestory, light flooded up into the hammerbeam roof, whose carved oak, surviving five hundred years, had turned to the colour of a field of ripe barley. The beams rested on stone corbels, carved in the likeness of angels, with just such blunt, homely Anglo-Saxon faces as those. in the pews below.

It was a beautiful church, but a simple one, with no pompous marble monuments, but a curious old font, built of the local brick, with high steps. Ours was a reverent but not a doleful congregation – there were as many in tweeds as in dark serge – and the sidesman who led us to a pew had a face burnt golden by the wind and sun. Still the bell tolled, and it was so quiet between the strokes that, sitting near a window, you could hear the rustle of a swallow darting to its nest beneath the eaves – almost hear the wings of a new-born butterfly, as it fluttered against the glass, and then poised itself among the flowers on the sill. The little organ at the back of the church started to play a slow melody, and presently the bell tolled its last stroke. We heard the shuffle of the bearers' feet in the porch, and the first words of the service: 'I am the resurrection and the life, saith the Lord'.

As for what followed, I remember no service that better fulfilled those words or made them easier to believe. Here were the mortal remains of a faithful man who had lived his three score years and ten in this village, had been devoted to this church, and had loved his fellow men. He could see the humour of their character, and had the gift of putting it into words, in the rich dialect he had spoken from childhood. Because of that gift he had become famous in his county, and people had come from far to this service in his memory. Their motive was affection, because that was also his motive. His laughter was never hurtful, and he often spoke a simple faith in humorous parables.

He liked to sing in the church choir, and the congregation sang 'The Lord is my shepherd', that most loved and familiar psalm, so that you could imagine him singing with them in honest enjoyment. The panoply of gloom at funerals has always been more like a relic of the old, dark gods than an expression of the Christian faith.

'Not to be sorry, as men without hope' – it seemed, as the bearers passed from the sunlit church, that one of God's cheerful men had spoken his last homely parable, and all Nature had conspired that day to illustrate it. The service was an act of piety, but not of gloom. It was saying, as our villagers still say when they go home at the end of the day's work, 'Fare ye well'.


Jonathan Mardle May, 1958

## Also available

*The Boy John Letters* – a CD in which Keith Skipper reads twelve of Sidney Grapes' Boy John Letters, with Sheilah Olley as Aunt Agatha.

*More Letters from The Boy John* – a second CD collection: Keith Skipper reads a further twelve of the Boy John Letters, with Sheilah Olley as Aunt Agatha.

Both available from Mousehold Press at £9.99 each.

*Broad Norfolk* – republished by popular demand, the original classic book on Norfolk dialect, written by Jonathan Mardle (Eric Fowler) of *Eastern Daily Press* fame and delightfully illustrated by Joe Lee. Described as 'one of the most important contributions ever made to Norfolk dialect'.

Published by Prospect Press at £5.95

# THE BOY JOHN LETTERS
## by Sidney Grapes

## A Fresh Delivery from Keith Skipper

Sidney Grapes had already made his mark as the archetypal Norfolk comedian at local concerts and dinners long before he dropped a few lines to the *Eastern Daily Press* in January 1946 under his pen-name 'The Boy John'. This was the start of a twelve-year correspondence during which time 88 'Boy John' letters were published. Written in Norfolk dialect, these were the work of a countryman who wrote as he spoke and spelt as he pleased, and their cast list quickly became household names: Boy John, Granfar, Aunt Agatha and the cantankerous Oul Mrs.W—.

This new collection underlines the abiding attraction of the Boy John Letters. For all that they may be rooted in time and in the Norfolk countryside, they retain genuine charm: they are wholly unpretentious, gently amusing, and admirably self-effacing; above all, they were written by a man who knew intimately the lives of the people he wrote about for he lived all his life among them.

### Bouquets for the Boy John Letters

"A work of not a little genius" – Peter Trudgill, Professor of Linguistics, University of Fribourg

"His characters were talked of as living people" – Jonathan Mardle, *Eastern Daily Press*

"An incomparable teller of good stories" – Rt Revd Percy Herbert, Bishop of Norwich, 1942–59

Broadcaster, writer and entertainer, Keith Skipper was founder-Chairman of FOND – Friends of Norfolk Dialect – and the Boy John Letters have featured frequently in his popular Press Gang shows around the County. His passionate commitment to Norfolk's cause has been underlined by his appointment as a Deputy Lieutenant of Norfolk and his award of an MBE for services to the Norfolk community in 2007.

Mousehold Press
£10.95

ISBN 978-1-874739-29-6

9 781874 739296

P.S. Aunt Agatha, she say: 'Thass wholly nice ter be remembered arter all this tyme.'